INDEX

D1244936

125

125C

125/125C

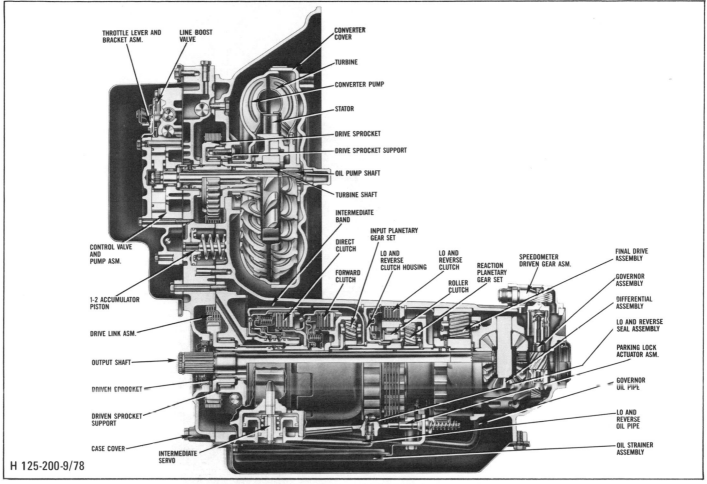

Figure 1 - Cut-away View THM 125 Transmission

GENERAL DESCRIPTION

The Turbo Hydra-matic 125 automatic transaxle transmission is engineered for use as a transverse mounted front wheel drive unit. It is specifically designed for use with small engines and is lighter in weight than other transmissions previously used with small engines. The unit has three forward gear ratios and one reverse, in addition to Neutral and Park. It is unique in that the differential and final drive gears are located within the transmission.

The THM 125 has three planetary gear sets and one differential gear set. Three multiple plate clutches, a band assembly and a roller clutch for friction elements are used to provide the proper operation of the planetary gear sets (Fig. 1).

A torque converter smoothly couples through oil the engine power to the gear train and hydraulically provides additional torque multiplication when required. The compound planetary gear set provides the three forward and one reverse gear ratios. Changing of the gear ratios is fully automatic in relation to vehicle speed and throttle position. Signals are constantly fed to the transmission to provide the proper gear ratio for maximum efficiency and performance at all throttle openings. The quadrant has six positions indicated in the following order: P, R, N, D, I, L (Fig. 2).

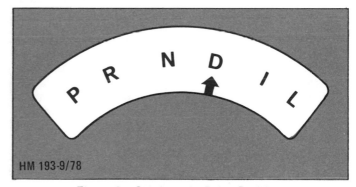

Figure 2 - Quadrant in Drive Position

P — Park position enables the transmission output (axle) shaft to be locked—thus preventing the vehicle from rolling either forward or backward. (For safety reasons, the vehicle parking brake should be used in addition to the transmission "Park" position.) Because the output (axle) shaft is mechanically locked by a parking pawl anchored in the case, the park position should not be selected until the vehicle has come to a stop. The engine may be started in the Park position.

R — Reverse enables the vehicle to be operated in a rearward direction.

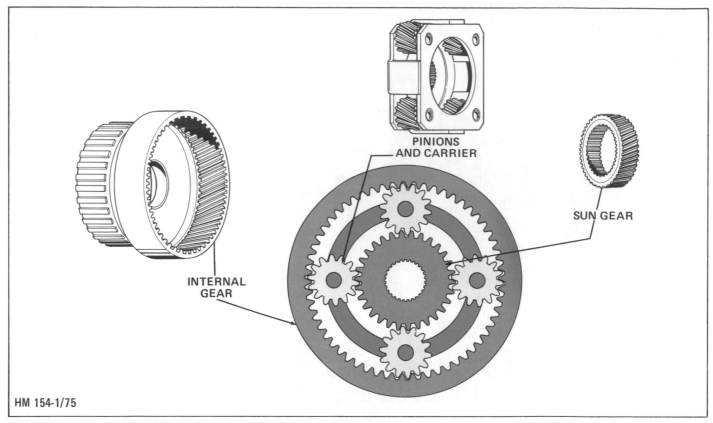

PINIONS
AND CARRIER

SUN GEAR

INTERNAL
GEAR

HM 154-1/75

Figure 3 - Planetary Gear Set

N — Neutral position enables the engine to be started and operated without driving the vehicle. If necessary, this position should be selected if the engine has to be restarted while the vehicle is moving.

D — Drive range is used for all normal driving conditions and maximum economy. Drive range has three gear ratios, from the starting ratio to direct drive. Downshifts to a lower ratio are available for safe passing by depressing the accelerator fully to the floor.

I * — Intermediate range adds new performance for congested traffic or hilly terrain. It has the same starting ratio as Drive range, but prevents the transmission from shifting above second gear, thus retaining second gear for acceleration or engine braking as desired. Intermediate range can be selected at any vehicle speed. The transmission will shift to second gear immediately and remain in second until the vehicle speed or the throttle position is changed to obtain first gear operation in the same manner as in Drive range.

L ⁑ — Lo Range can be selected at any vehicle speed. The transmission will shift to second gear immediately and remains in second until vehicle speed is reduced to approximately 40 mph (64 km/h)+, at which time the transmission will shift to first gear. This is particularly beneficial for maintaining maximum engine braking such as descending steep grades.

*   Sometimes marked S or L_2

⁑   Sometimes marked L_1

+   Km/h (Kilometer per hour) is a metric unit of measure for speed.

PRINCIPLES OF OPERATION

The purpose of an automobile transmission is to provide neutral, reverse, and forward driving ranges that increase the torque or twisting force from the engine to the driving wheels as required for greater pulling power and performance.

Basically, an automobile transmission is a form of lever that enables the engine to move heavy loads with less effort. As the heavy load or vehicle begins to move, less leverage or ratio is required to keep it moving.

By providing a suitable number of levers or torque multiplying ratios, improved performance and economy are possible over the entire driving range. Changing the ratio automatically relieves the driver of the responsibility of selecting the best possible ratio for each condition and makes driving safer and easier.

PLANETARY GEARS

Planetary gears are used in the THM 125 transmission as the basic means of multiplying the twisting force or torque of the engine. Planetary gears are so named because of their physical arrangement. They are always in mesh and thus cannot "clash" like other gears that go in and out of mesh. The gears are designed so that several gear teeth are in mesh or in contact at once. This distributes the forces over several teeth for greater strength. Because the shafts generally used with planetary gear trains can be arranged on the same centerline, a very compact unit is obtained.

4

A planetary gear train consists of a center or sun gear, an internal gear (so called because of its internally cut teeth), and a planetary carrier assembly which includes and supports the smaller planet gears called pinions (Fig. 3).

A planetary gear train can be used to increase torque, increase speed, reverse the direction of rotation, or function as a coupling or connector for direct drive.

Increasing the twisting force or torque is generally known as operating in reduction, because there is always a decrease in the speed of the output member which is proportional to the increase in the output torque.

Stated in another way, with a constant input speed, the output torque increases as the output speed decreases.

REDUCTION

When the sun gear is held stationary and power is applied to the internal gear in a clockwise direction, the planetary pinions rotate in a clockwise direction and "walk" around the stationary sun gear, thus rotating the carrier assembly clockwise in reduction (Fig. 4).

DIRECT DRIVE

Direct drive is obtained when any two members of the planetary gear train rotate in the same direction at the same speed. This forces the third member to turn at the same speed. In this condition, the pinions do not rotate on their pins, but act as wedges to lock the entire unit together as one rotating part (Fig. 5).

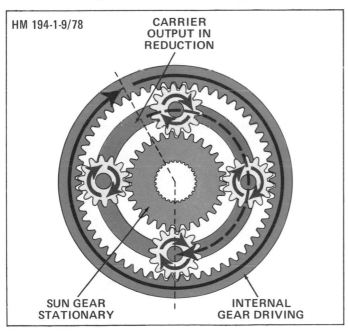

Figure 4 - Reduction

REVERSAL OF DIRECTION

A reversal of direction is obtained whenever the carrier is restrained from spinning free and power is applied to either the sun gear or internal gear. This causes the planet pinions to act as idlers, thus driving the output member in the opposite direction (Fig. 6).

In both cases, the output member is turning in a direction opposite the input member.

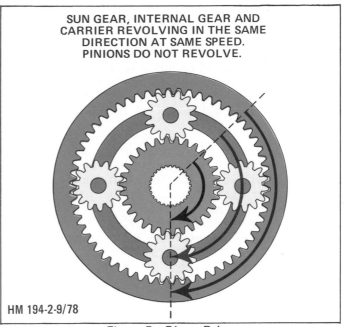

Figure 5 - Direct Drive

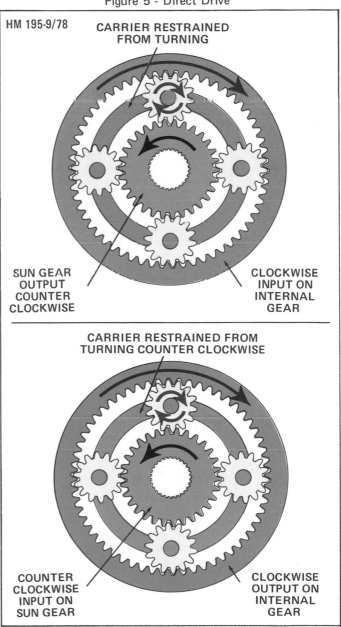

Figure 6 - Reversal of Direction

5

TORQUE CONVERTER

The torque converter serves two primary functions. First, it acts as a fluid coupling to smoothly connect engine power through oil to the transmission gear train. Second, it multiplies the torque or twisting effort from the engine when additional performance is desired.

The torque converter consists of three basic elements: the pump (driving member), the turbine (driven member), and the stator (reaction member) (Fig. 7). The converter cover is welded to the pump to seal all three members in an oil filled housing. The converter cover is bolted to the engine flexplate which is bolted directly to the engine crankshaft. The converter pump is, therefore, mechanically connected to the engine and turns at engine speed whenever the engine is operating.

When the engine is running and the converter pump is spinning, it acts as a centrifugal pump, picking up oil at its center and discharging this oil at its rim between the blades (Fig. 8). The shape of the converter pump shells and blades causes this oil to leave the pump spinning in a clockwise direction toward the blades of the turbine. As the oil strikes the turbine blades, it imparts a force to the turbine causing it to turn. When the engine is idling and the converter pump is not spinning fast, the force of the oil leaving the pump is not great enough to turn the turbine with any efficiency. This allows the vehicle to stand in gear with the engine idling. As the throttle is opened and the pump speed increases, the force of the oil increases and engine power is more efficiently transmitted to the turbine member and the gear train.

After the oil has imparted its force to the turbine, it follows the contour of the turbine shell and blades so that it leaves the center section of the turbine spinning counter-clockwise in a direction opposite to engine rotation.

The force or torque delivered from the engine is absorbed by the turbine when it reverses the clockwise spinning oil from the converter pump. If the counter-clockwise spinning oil from the turbine was allowed to continue to the inner section of the converter pump, it would strike the blades of the pump in a direction that would hinder it and engine rotation, and consequently reduce the force the converter pump could deliver to the oil. To prevent this from happening, a stator assembly is added.

The stator is located between the pump and turbine and is mounted on a one-way or roller clutch which allows it to rotate clockwise but not counter-clockwise (Fig. 9).

The purpose of the stator is to re-direct the oil returning from the turbine and change its direction of rotation back to that of the pump member. The energy of the oil is then used to assist the engine in turning the pump. This increases the force of the oil driving the turbine; and as a result, multiplies the torque or twisting force from the engine.

The force of the oil flowing from the turbine to the blades of the stator tends to rotate the stator counter-clockwise, but the roller clutch prevents it from turning (Fig. 10).

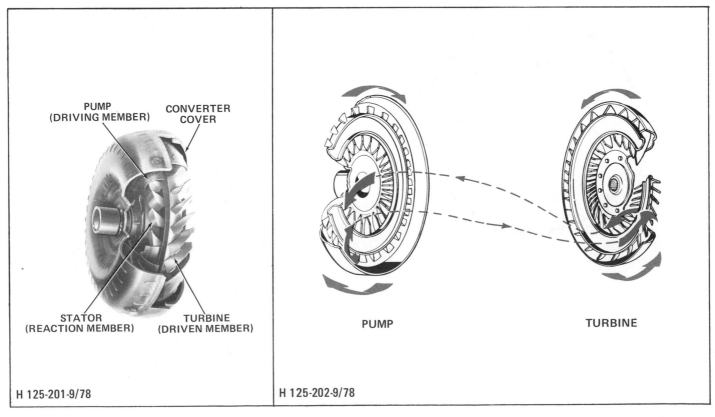

PUMP (DRIVING MEMBER)   CONVERTER COVER

STATOR (REACTION MEMBER)   TURBINE (DRIVEN MEMBER)

H 125-201-9/78

PUMP   TURBINE

H 125-202-9/78

Figure 7 - Torque Converter Assembly

Figure 8 - Oil Flow without Stator

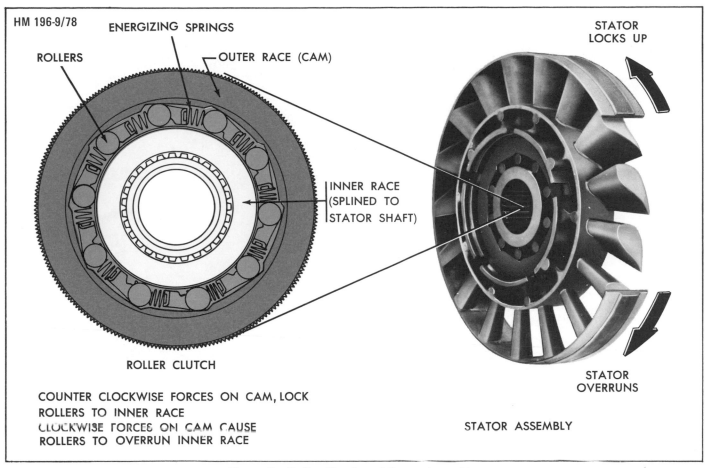

ROLLERS

ENERGIZING SPRINGS

OUTER RACE (CAM)

STATOR LOCKS UP

INNER RACE (SPLINED TO STATOR SHAFT)

STATOR OVERRUNS

ROLLER CLUTCH

STATOR ASSEMBLY

COUNTER CLOCKWISE FORCES ON CAM, LOCK ROLLERS TO INNER RACE
CLOCKWISE FORCES ON CAM CAUSE ROLLERS TO OVERRUN INNER RACE

Figure 9 - Roller Clutch and Stator Assembly

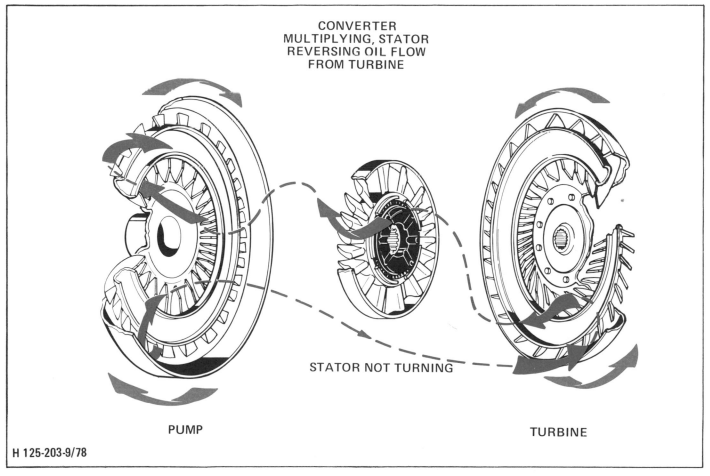

CONVERTER MULTIPLYING, STATOR REVERSING OIL FLOW FROM TURBINE

STATOR NOT TURNING

PUMP

TURBINE

H 125-203-9/78

Figure 10 - Oil Flow with Stator Active

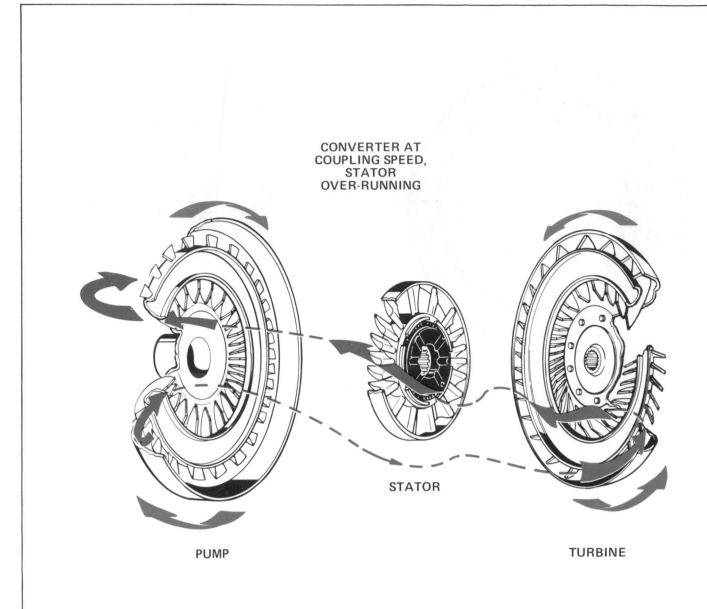

CONVERTER AT
COUPLING SPEED,
STATOR
OVER-RUNNING

STATOR

PUMP

TURBINE

H 125-204-9/78

Figure 11 - Oil Flow with Stator Spinning

With the engine operating at full throttle, transmission in gear, and the vehicle standing still, the converter is capable of multiplying engine torque by approximately 1.95:1.

As turbine speed and vehicle speed increases, the direction of the oil leaving the turbine changes (Fig. 11). The oil flows against the rear side of the stator vanes in a clockwise direction. Since the stator is now impeding the smooth flow of oil, the roller clutch automatically releases and the stator revolves freely on its shaft. Once the stator becomes inactive, there is no further multiplication of engine torque within the converter. At this point the converter is merely acting as a fluid coupling as both the converter pump and the turbine are turning at approximately the same speed.

POWER FLOW

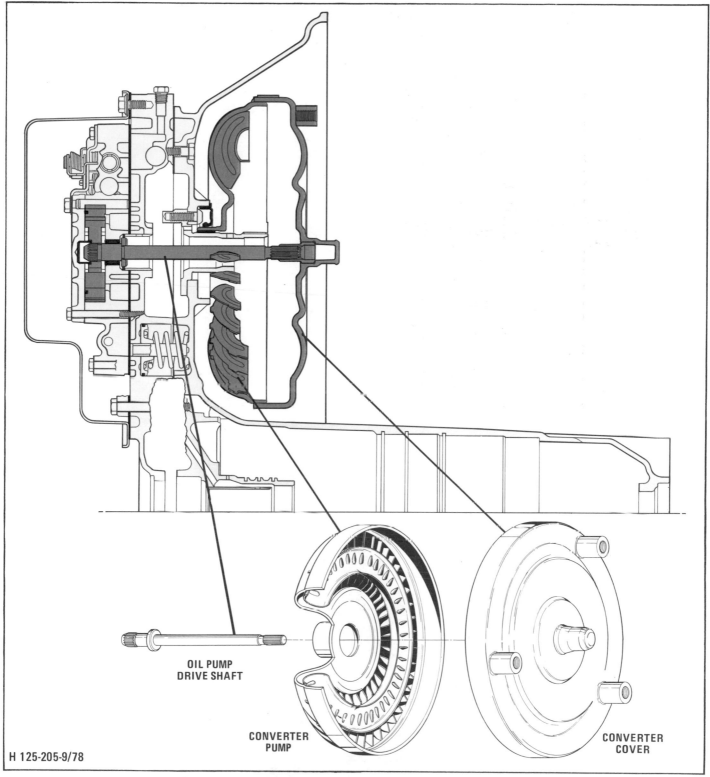

OIL PUMP
DRIVE SHAFT

CONVERTER
PUMP

CONVERTER
COVER

H 125-205-9/78

Figure 12 - Converter Cover and Pump, and Oil Pump Drive Shaft

The power flow and the principles of operation of the THM 125 transmission power train are most easily understood when each unit or component is considered separately with a part by part build up of the total unit.

TORQUE CONVERTER

To use the power available from the engine, the torque converter cover is bolted to the engine flexplate or flywheel. The converter cover is welded to the converter pump, thus making the converter pump directly

driven by the engine (Fig. 12). The converter pump is driven in a clockwise direction when viewed from the front of the engine (or right front fender, since the engine is transversely mounted).

The oil pump drive shaft is splined to the converter cover at one end, while the other end is splined to the transmission oil pump. This arrangement means that the transmission oil pump is also driven directly by the engine and will operate at engine speed.

9

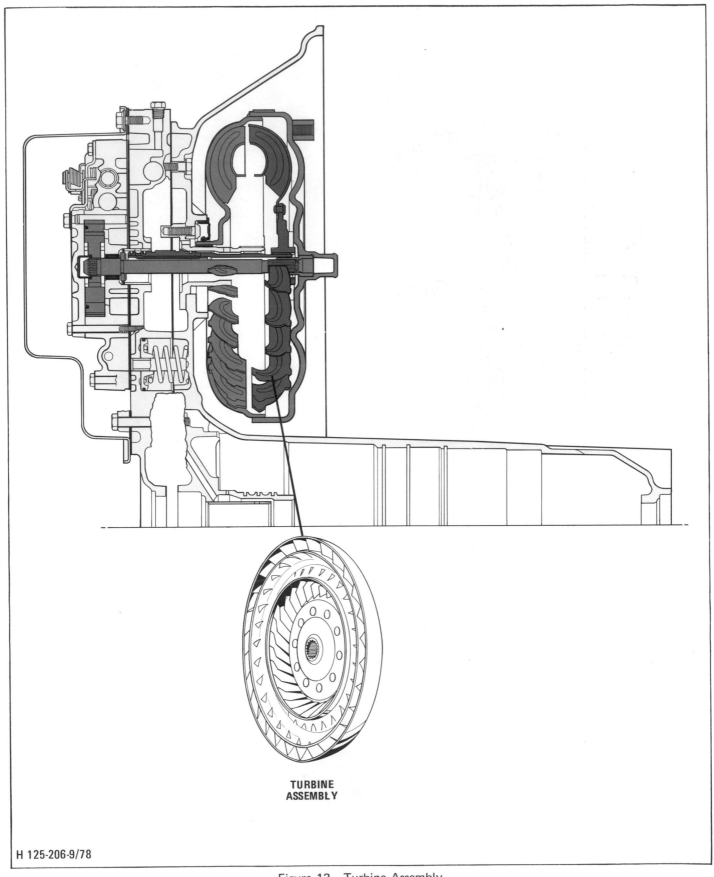

TURBINE ASSEMBLY

Figure 13 - Turbine Assembly

H 125-206-9/78

The converter driven member or turbine is located within the converter housing in front of the pump member (Fig. 13), and its blades face the pump blades. As the pump member turns with oil in the converter, the force of the oil from the pump strikes the blades of the turbine, thus imparting a driving force causing it to turn.

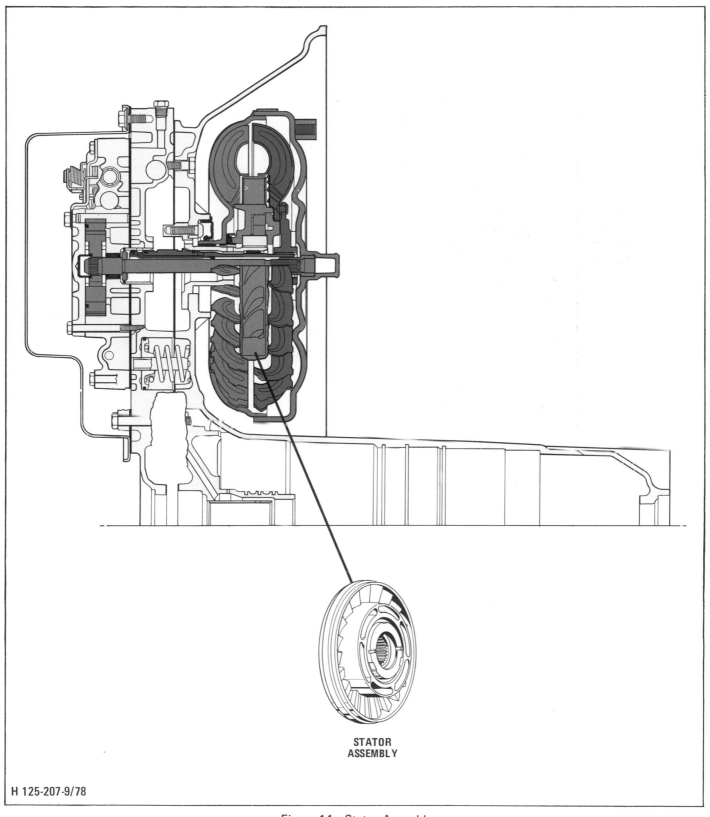

STATOR
ASSEMBLY

H 125-207-9/78

Figure 14 - Stator Assembly

The converter stator assembly is installed between the turbine and the pump member (Fig. 14). It is located so that its blades receive the oil as it passes from the turbine to the pump. The stator shaft, which is part of the drive sprocket support, provides the support for the fixed or inner race of the roller clutch assembly. The oil flow which tends to rotate the stator counterclockwise, locks the roller clutch and holds the stator in place. Oil flow from the turbine that tends to turn the stator clockwise causes the roller clutch to overrun, allowing the stator to rotate freely with the oil.

The turbine shaft is splined into the converter hub and delivers the converter's output torque to the transmission drive sprocket.

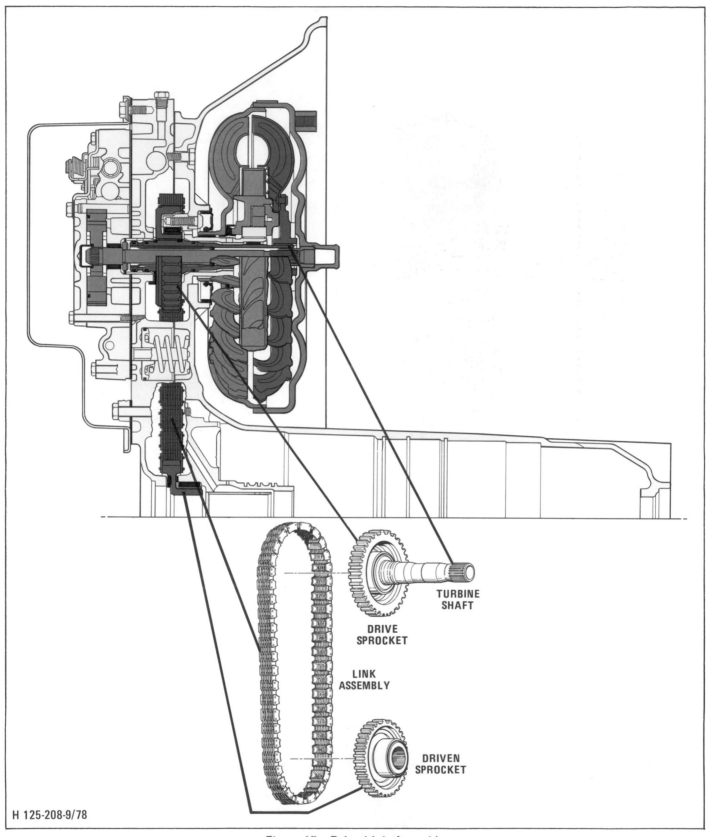

Figure 15 - Drive Link Assembly

A drive link assembly (chain) connects the drive and driven sprockets, and provides the connection from the torque converter to the transmission power train (Fig. 15). The drive and driven sprockets may have a different number of teeth according to engine size to deliver the desired torque to the transmission power train.

Actually, the torque converter and drive link assembly form a simple type of transmission as the converter pump is the input and the driven sprocket is the output. The needs of an automobile transmission are greater, however, in that some means of providing additional torque multiplication, reverse and neutral are required.

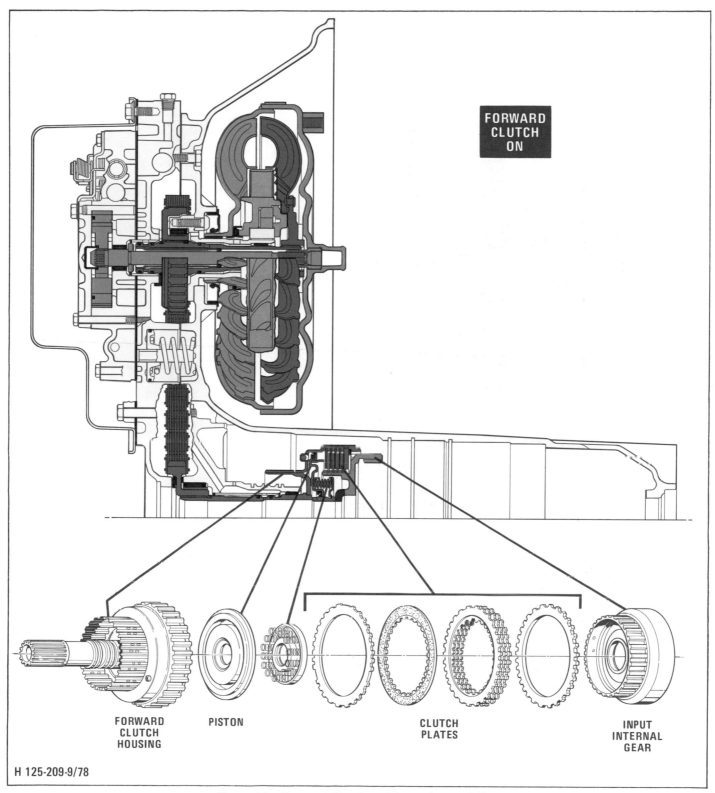

H 125-209-9/78

Figure 16 - Forward Clutch and Input Internal Gear

FORWARD CLUTCH

To provide a means of connecting and disconnecting power output from the converter to the transmission gear train, a forward clutch is used (Fig. 16). The forward clutch is composed of a forward clutch housing which is welded to the input shaft; steel clutch plates which are tanged into the forward clutch housing; composition faced clutch plates which are splined to the clutch hub which is part of the input internal gear; a clutch piston that hydraulically applies to lock the plates together; and release springs that retract the piston to release the clutch when the hydraulic pressure is exhausted. Whenever the forward clutch is applied, power from the converter through the drive link assembly and the input shaft is connected to the internal gear of the input gear set. Releasing the forward clutch interrupts the connection between the converter and the input internal gear, placing the transmission in neutral.

13

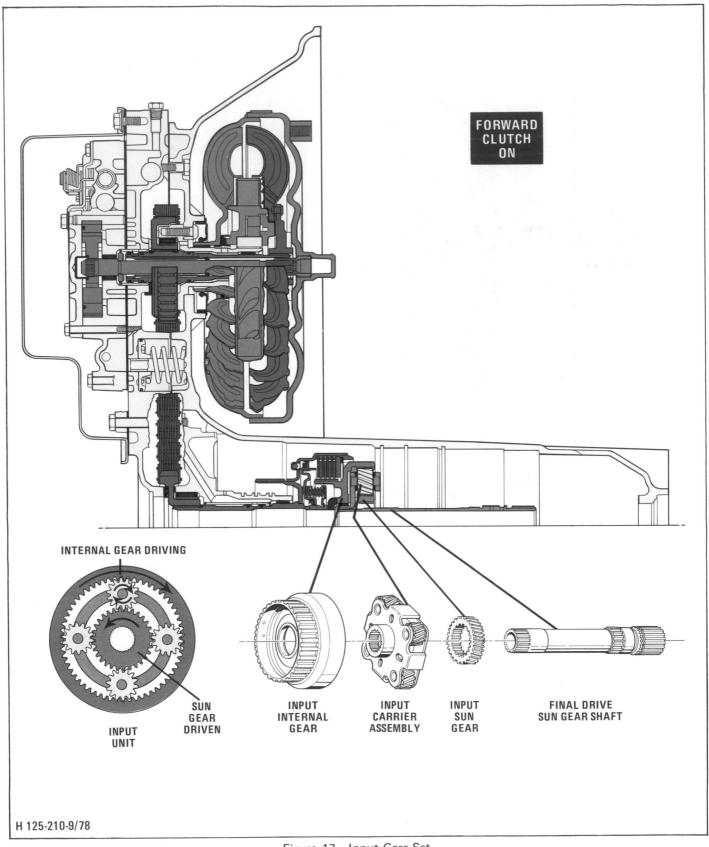

FORWARD
CLUTCH
ON

INTERNAL GEAR DRIVING

INPUT
UNIT

SUN
GEAR
DRIVEN

INPUT
INTERNAL
GEAR

INPUT
CARRIER
ASSEMBLY

INPUT
SUN
GEAR

FINAL DRIVE
SUN GEAR SHAFT

H 125-210-9/78

Figure 17 - Input Gear Set

PLANETARY GEAR SET

The input unit of the compound planetary gear set consists of an input internal gear which is part of the forward clutch hub, an input carrier and pinion assembly, and an input sun gear (Fig. 17). The input carrier is splined to the final drive sun gear shaft.

Power through the forward clutch causes the input internal gear to drive in a clockwise direction. This rotates the planet pinions as idlers in a clockwise direction and drives the input sun gear in a counter-clockwise direction.

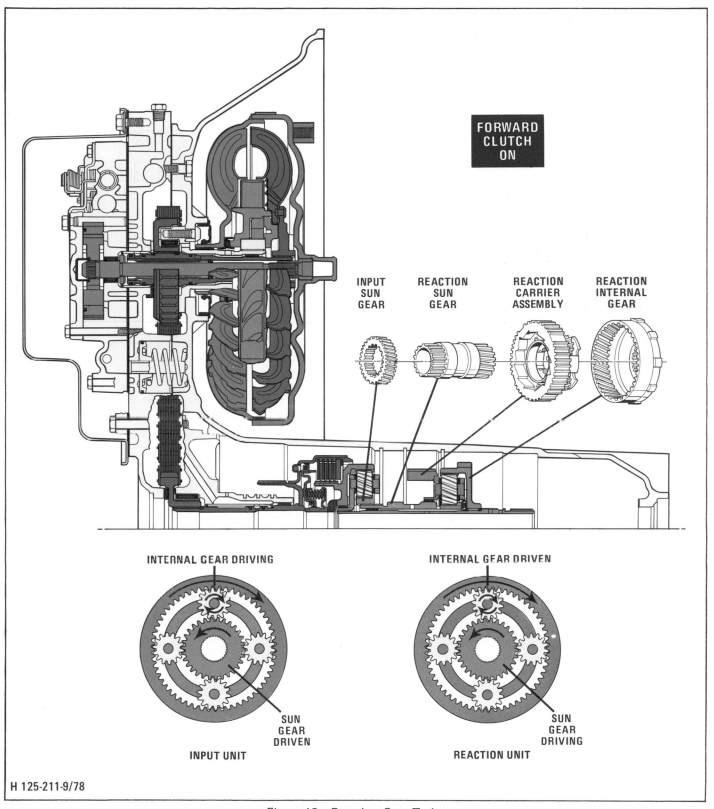

FORWARD CLUTCH ON

INPUT SUN GEAR

REACTION SUN GEAR

REACTION CARRIER ASSEMBLY

REACTION INTERNAL GEAR

INTERNAL GEAR DRIVING

INTERNAL GEAR DRIVEN

SUN GEAR DRIVEN

SUN GEAR DRIVING

INPUT UNIT

REACTION UNIT

H 125-211-9/78

Figure 18 - Reaction Gear Train

The input sun gear is splined to the reaction sun gear so the reaction sun gear now turns counter-clockwise (Fig. 18). This drives the planet pinions in the reaction carrier in a clockwise rotation, which in turn applies a force that tends to drive the reaction internal gear clockwise.

The reaction internal gear is splined to the final drive sun gear shaft and this reacts with the force of the carrier pinions which are trying to drive the reaction internal gear clock-wise. This force wants to turn the entire carrier assembly counter-clockwise instead of turning the reaction internal gear and final drive sun gear shaft against the weight of the vehicle. To make the gear set effective in driving the vehicle, something has to hold the reaction carrier stationary.

15

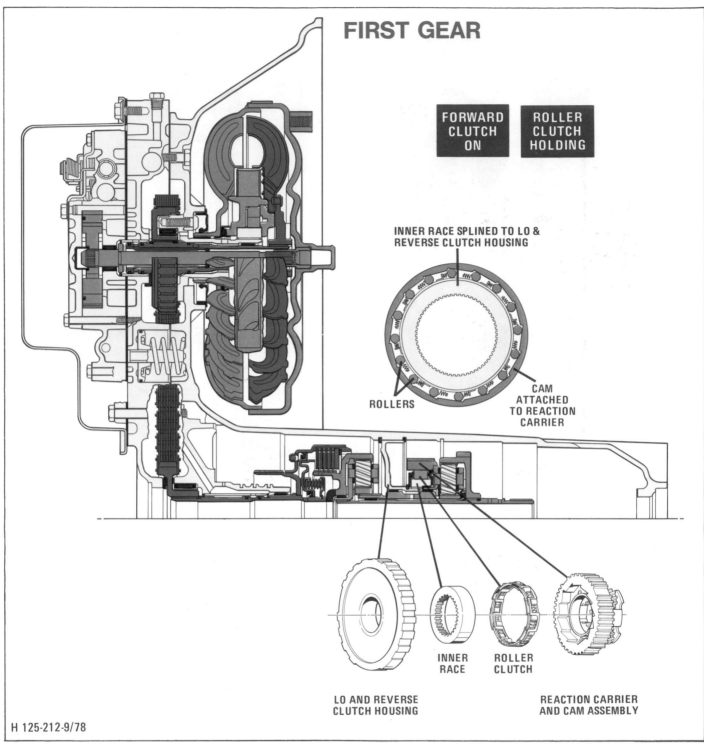

FIRST GEAR

FORWARD CLUTCH ON

ROLLER CLUTCH HOLDING

INNER RACE SPLINED TO LO & REVERSE CLUTCH HOUSING

CAM ATTACHED TO REACTION CARRIER

ROLLERS

INNER RACE

ROLLER CLUTCH

LO AND REVERSE CLUTCH HOUSING

REACTION CARRIER AND CAM ASSEMBLY

Figure 19 - Roller Clutch

ROLLER CLUTCH

A roller clutch assembly is used to hold the reaction carrier fixed against counter-clockwise rotation (Fig. 19). A roller clutch is a type of one-way clutch that allows a rotating part to turn in one direction, but not in the other. In this application, the inner race is splined to the lo and reverse clutch housing, which is splined into the transmission case and held in place by a snap ring. The roller clutch cam is welded to the reaction carrier.

The roller clutch assembly is installed between the race and cam in such a way that it prevents the reaction carrier from rotating counter-clockwise. This provides the required force to hold the reaction carrier

and causes the reaction planet pinions to drive the reaction internal gear and final drive sun gear shaft clockwise, in reduction at a ratio of approximately 2.84:1. This gear reduction, combined with the maximum converter torque multiplication of approximately 1.95:1, gives an over-all transmission first gear starting ratio of approximately 5.54:1.

As vehicle speed increases, less torque multiplication is needed for maximum efficiency. Thus, it is desirable to shift the transmission to a lower gear ratio or second gear (Fig. 20). This is accomplished by adding the input drum, the direct clutch housing and the intermediate band.

SECOND GEAR

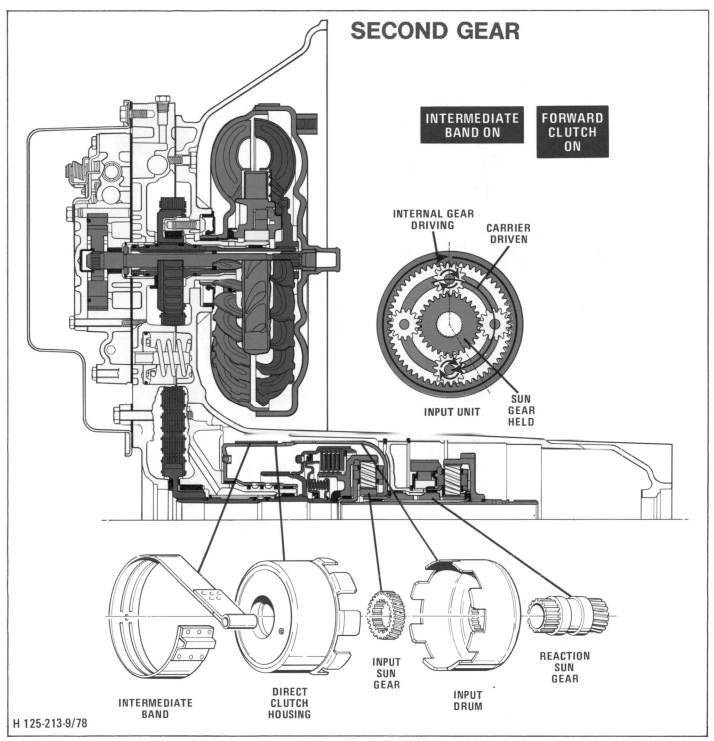

INTERMEDIATE BAND ON

FORWARD CLUTCH ON

INTERNAL GEAR DRIVING
CARRIER DRIVEN
SUN GEAR HELD
INPUT UNIT

INTERMEDIATE BAND

DIRECT CLUTCH HOUSING

INPUT SUN GEAR

INPUT DRUM

REACTION SUN GEAR

H 125-213-9/78

Figure 20 - Intermediate Band, Direct Clutch Housing and Input Drum

INTERMEDIATE BAND

The input drum is splined to the sun gears and is tanged to the direct clutch housing. The intermediate band is wrapped around the direct clutch housing. When the intermediate band is hydraulically applied, it prevents the direct clutch housing, input drum, and sun gears from rotating.

When the sun gears are held, power flow becomes as follows:

Converter output is transmitted through the drive link assembly to the forward clutch, and through the forward clutch to the input internal gear in a clockwise direction. As the input internal gear turns clockwise, the input carrier pinions rotate clockwise on their pins and walk around the

stationary sun gear. This turns the input carrier (which is splined to the final drive sun gear shaft) and the final drive sun gear shaft in a clockwise direction at a reduced speed in a gear ratio of approximately 1.60:1 or second gear.

The reaction gear set is not loaded or working during second gear operation. However, because the input carrier and the reaction internal gear are both splined to the final drive sun gear shaft, the reaction internal gear is running clockwise in reduction. This causes the reaction planet pinions to run clockwise around the stationary sun gear turning the reaction carrier clockwise. This clockwise rotation of the carrier causes the roller clutch to over-run.

THIRD GEAR

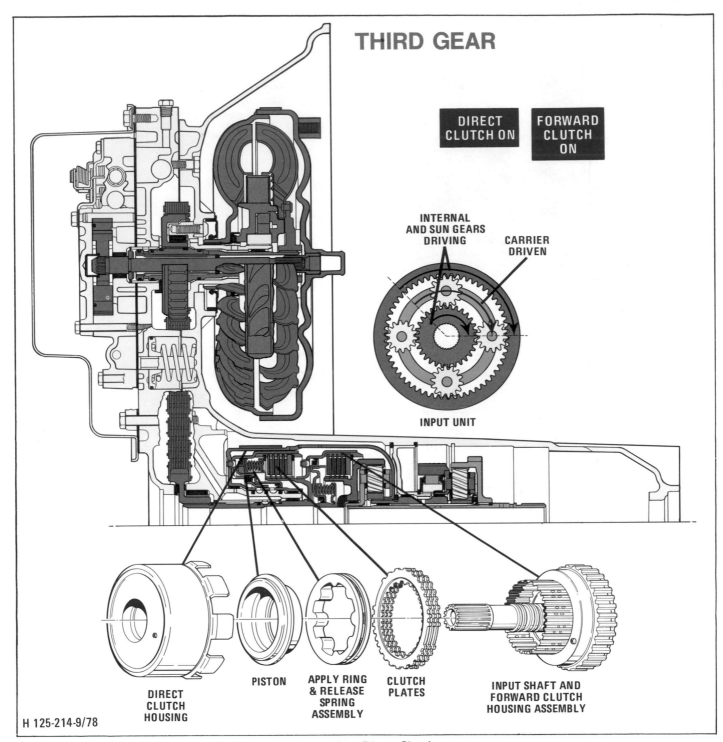

DIRECT CLUTCH ON   FORWARD CLUTCH ON

INTERNAL AND SUN GEARS DRIVING

CARRIER DRIVEN

INPUT UNIT

DIRECT CLUTCH HOUSING

PISTON

APPLY RING & RELEASE SPRING ASSEMBLY

CLUTCH PLATES

INPUT SHAFT AND FORWARD CLUTCH HOUSING ASSEMBLY

H 125-214-9/78

Figure 21 - Direct Clutch

As the vehicle continues to accelerate, a speed is attained where the 1.60:1 transmission gear ratio is no longer required or desired. The transmission is then shifted to third gear or direct drive. Direct drive results when the input internal gear and the sun gears are driven at the same speed by the addition of a direct clutch assembly (Fig. 21).

The direct clutch composition-faced clutch plates are splined to the direct clutch hub which is welded to the forward clutch housing. The steel clutch plates are splined to the direct clutch housing, which is tanged to the input drum, which is splined to the sun gears. The clutch is hydraulically applied by a piston that is located in the direct clutch housing. When the clutch

is applied, power from the forward clutch is divided to follow two paths to the gear set. First, the power continues through the forward clutch to the input internal gear. Second, power from the forward clutch housing is transmitted through the direct clutch to the input drum and the sun gears. This forces the input carrier to turn at the same speed. In this condition, the planet pinions do not rotate on their pins, but act as wedges to lock the entire unit together as one rotating part.

The intermediate band is released as the direct clutch is applied for third gear to allow the direct clutch to drive the sun gear.

18

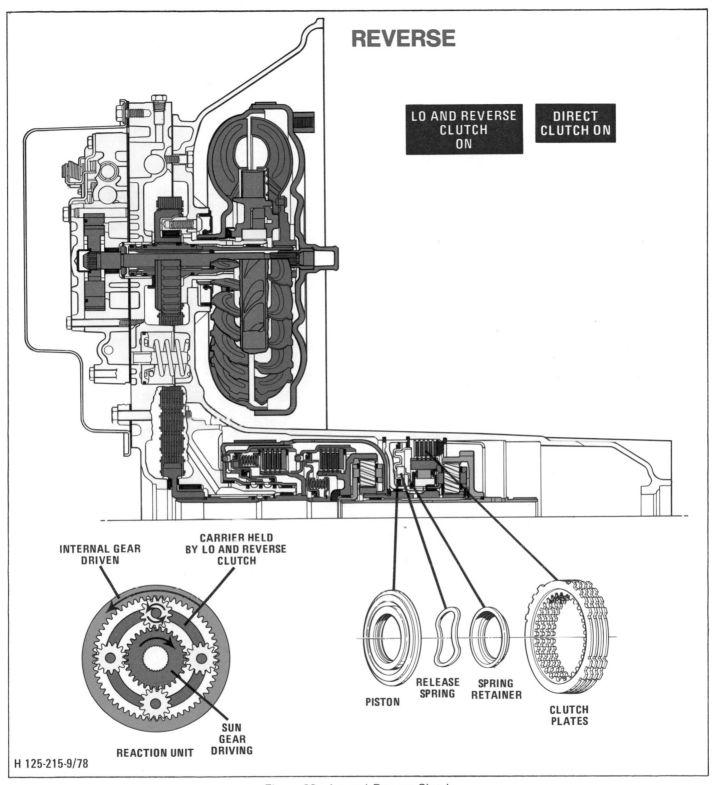

REVERSE

LO AND REVERSE CLUTCH ON   DIRECT CLUTCH ON

INTERNAL GEAR DRIVEN

CARRIER HELD BY LO AND REVERSE CLUTCH

SUN GEAR DRIVING

REACTION UNIT

PISTON   RELEASE SPRING   SPRING RETAINER   CLUTCH PLATES

H 125-215-9/78

Figure 22 - Lo and Reverse Clutch

LO AND REVERSE CLUTCH

In order to obtain reverse, the lo and reverse clutch assembly is added (Fig. 22). The lo and reverse clutch holds the reaction carrier against clockwise rotation which would cause the roller clutch to over-run. Power flow through the transmission in reverse is as follows:

The converter torque is transmitted through the drive link assembly to the forward clutch housing; the forward clutch is released and disconnects the flow of power to the input internal gear. Power flows from the forward clutch housing to the direct clutch hub; the direct clutch is applied; and power flows through the direct clutch housing and input drum to the sun gears in a clockwise direction. With the reaction sun gear driving clockwise and the reaction carrier held, the pinions revolve counterclockwise as idlers. This drives the reaction internal gear and final drive sun gear shaft counter-clockwise or in a reverse direction in reduction at a ratio of approximately 2.07:1. The over-all torque multiplication and gear reduction, is approximately 4.04:1.

INTERMEDIATE RANGE

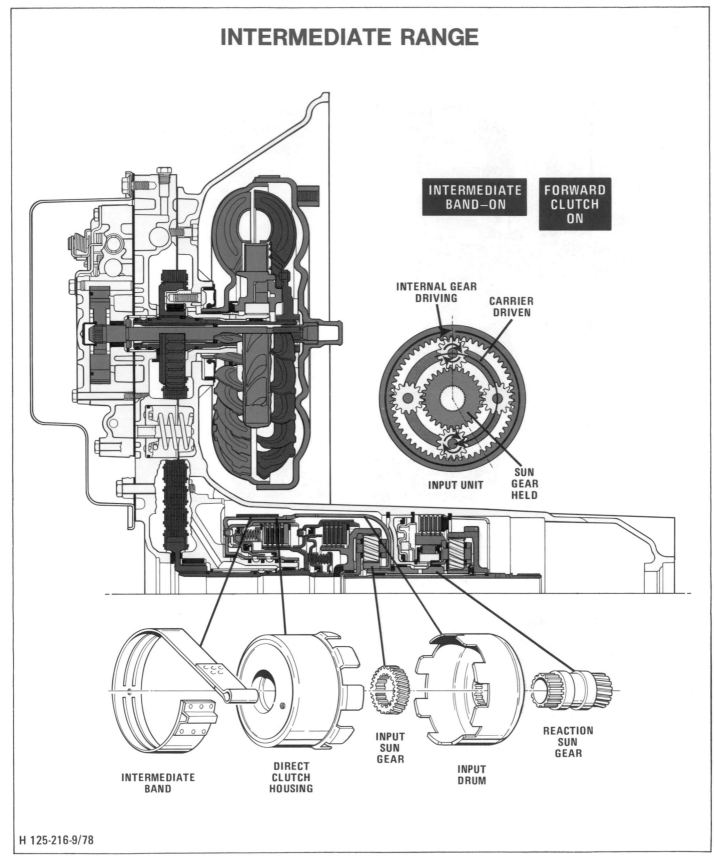

INTERMEDIATE BAND—ON   FORWARD CLUTCH ON

INTERNAL GEAR DRIVING

CARRIER DRIVEN

INPUT UNIT

SUN GEAR HELD

INTERMEDIATE BAND

DIRECT CLUTCH HOUSING

INPUT SUN GEAR

INPUT DRUM

REACTION SUN GEAR

H 125-216-9/78

Figure 23 - Intermediate Band, Direct Clutch Housing and Input Drum

ENGINE BRAKING

The THM 125 transmission and engine compression can also be used as an effective braking device when descending long grades (Fig. 23). While operating in Drive range, third gear, placing the selector lever in the Intermediate range will immediately shift the transmission into second gear. With the accelerator released and the transmission in second gear, the vehicle will decelerate using engine compression as a braking force.

LO RANGE
FIRST GEAR

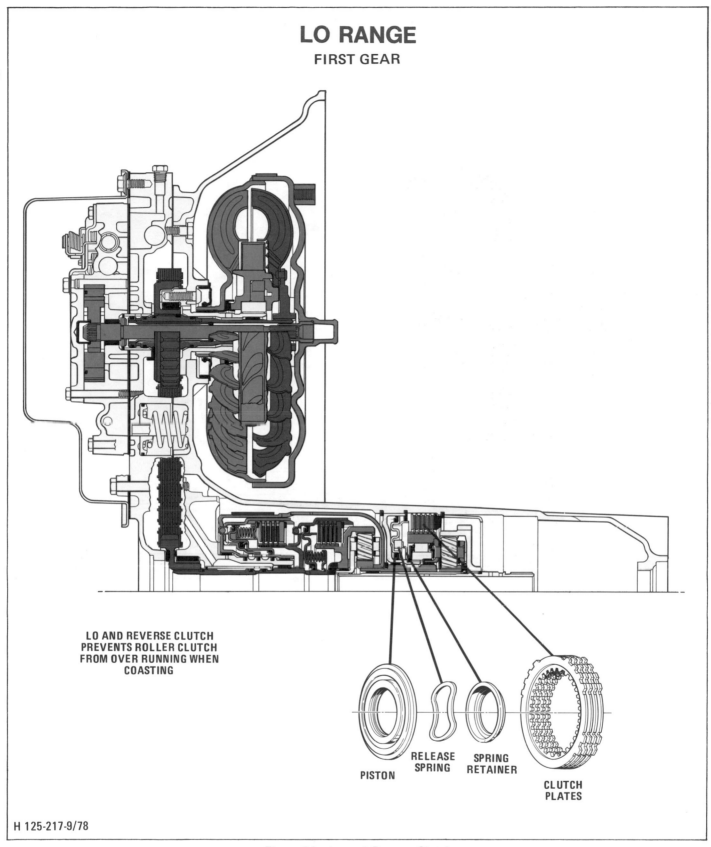

LO AND REVERSE CLUTCH
PREVENTS ROLLER CLUTCH
FROM OVER RUNNING WHEN
COASTING

PISTON RELEASE SPRING SPRING RETAINER CLUTCH PLATES

H 125-217-9/78

Figure 24 - Lo and Reverse Clutch

For even greater engine braking, the transmission can be placed in Lo range (Fig. 24). At speeds below approximately 40 mph (64 km/h), the transmission will shift to first gear. When the vehicle coasts in first gear, the front wheels are driving the transmission through the final drive sun gear shaft. With the power being applied through the final drive sun gear shaft, there is a natural tendency for the roller clutch to over-run. To prevent the reaction carrier from over-running the roller clutch, the lo and reverse clutch is applied and keeps the transmission in first gear to provide effective braking.

FINAL DRIVE

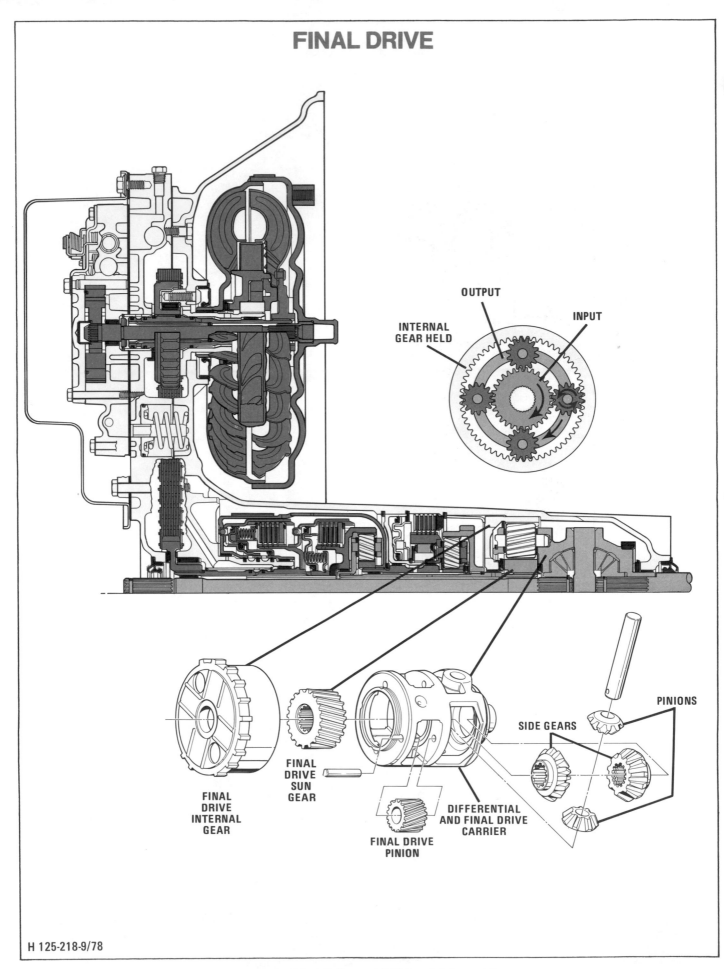

OUTPUT

INPUT

INTERNAL GEAR HELD

FINAL DRIVE INTERNAL GEAR

FINAL DRIVE SUN GEAR

FINAL DRIVE PINION

DIFFERENTIAL AND FINAL DRIVE CARRIER

SIDE GEARS

PINIONS

H 125-218-9/78

Figure 25 - Final Drive and Differential Assemblies

FINAL DRIVE AND DIFFERENTIAL ASSEMBLIES

Since the THM 125 is a transaxle transmission, it is necessary to have some means of transferring power from the final drive sun gear shaft to the front axle of the vehicle. This is done by a unit located at the output end of the gear train called the final drive and differential assembly. This unit of the THM 125 transmission is usually located in the rear axle assembly of a conventional vehicle.

FINAL DRIVE ASSEMBLY

The final drive assembly is a planetary gear set consisting of a final drive internal gear which is splined to the transmission case, a final drive sun gear which is splined to the final drive sun gear shaft, and the final drive planet pinions which are located in the differential and final drive carrier assembly (Fig. 25).

This gear set operates in reduction at all times. Power through the final drive sun gear shaft drives the sun gear in a clockwise direction which drives the planet pinions in a counter-clockwise direction. Since the final drive internal gear is splined to the case and will not rotate, the differential and final drive carrier assembly will rotate in a clockwise direction.

The gear ratio of approximately 2.84:1 performs the same function as the ring and pinion gears in a conventional rear axle unit. It is the fixed final or axle ratio that is required to match the engine power and drive train to the vehicle requirements in all normal operating conditions.

DIFFERENTIAL ASSEMBLY

The differential assembly provides the means for allowing one driving wheel to travel faster than the other when the vehicle is going around corners or curves. (The wheel on the outside of the curve has to turn faster). The differential consists of a differential and final drive carrier assembly and four bevel gears (Fig. 25). Two of the bevel gears, differential side gears, are connected to each of the output (axle) shafts. The other two gears, differential pinions, act as idlers to transfer the power from the carrier to the side gears. The pinion gears act to balance the power load between the differential side gears while allowing unequal speeds of axle rotation when the vehicle is in a curve. When the vehicle is driving straight ahead the pinion gears are not turning and the differential side gears rotate as a fixed unit with the differential and final drive carrier assembly (Fig. 26). The end result, in drive ranges, is a clockwise rotation of the two output (axle) shafts, moving the vehicle in a forward direction or counterclockwise for reverse.

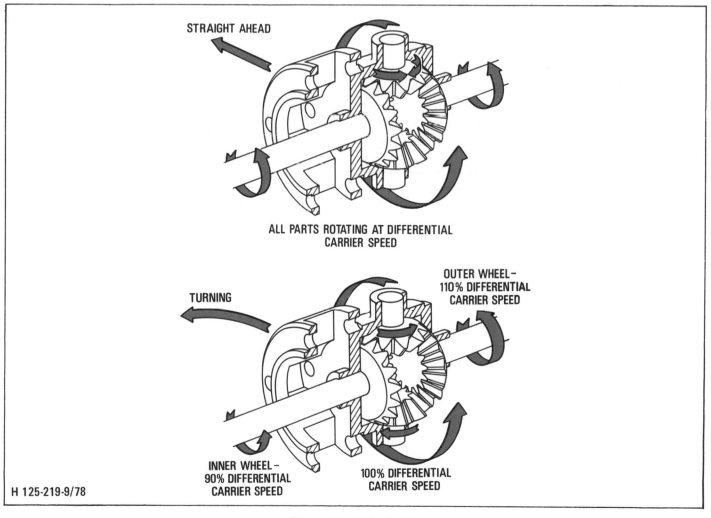

STRAIGHT AHEAD

ALL PARTS ROTATING AT DIFFERENTIAL CARRIER SPEED

TURNING

OUTER WHEEL – 110% DIFFERENTIAL CARRIER SPEED

INNER WHEEL – 90% DIFFERENTIAL CARRIER SPEED

100% DIFFERENTIAL CARRIER SPEED

H 125-219-9/78

Figure 26 - Differential

SUMMARY OF POWER FLOW

NEUTRAL-ENGINE RUNNING

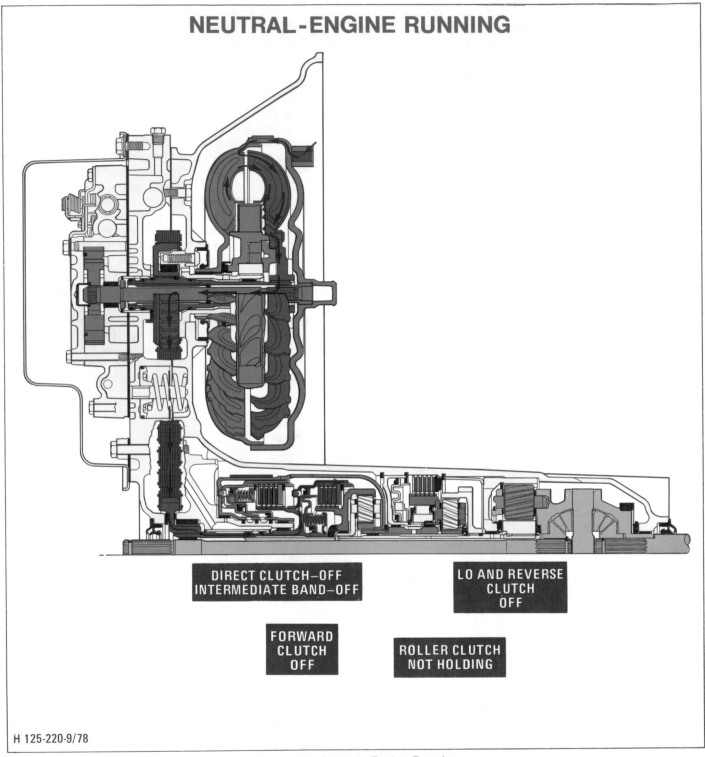

DIRECT CLUTCH—OFF
INTERMEDIATE BAND—OFF

LO AND REVERSE
CLUTCH
OFF

FORWARD
CLUTCH
OFF

ROLLER CLUTCH
NOT HOLDING

H 125-220-9/78

Figure 27 - Neutral—Engine Running

In Neutral, the band and all clutches are released; therefore, no power is transmitted from the forward clutch housing to the planetary gear train, which results in no power to the output (axle) shafts.

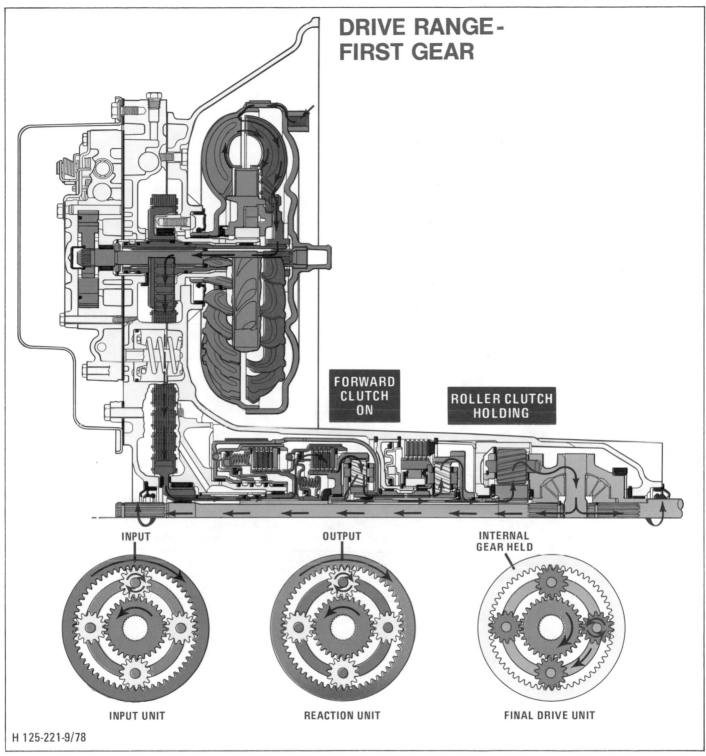

DRIVE RANGE- FIRST GEAR

FORWARD CLUTCH ON

ROLLER CLUTCH HOLDING

INPUT	OUTPUT	INTERNAL GEAR HELD
INPUT UNIT	REACTION UNIT	FINAL DRIVE UNIT

H 125-221-9/78

Figure 28 - Drive Range—First Gear

FORWARD CLUTCH—APPLIED

With the selector lever in Drive range, the forward clutch is applied. This delivers converter torque through the drive link assembly and forward clutch to the input internal gear in a clockwise direction. (Converter torque is about 1.95 times engine torque at stall.)

Clockwise rotation of the input internal gear causes the input pinions to turn clockwise, driving the input sun gear counter-clockwise. In turn, the reaction sun gear drives the reaction pinions clockwise, which

ROLLER CLUTCH—HOLDING

drives the reaction internal gear and final drive sun gear shaft clockwise in a reduction of approximately 2.84:1. The reaction carrier is being held by the roller clutch. (Approximate stall ratio equals 5.54:1.)

The final drive sun gear shaft drives the final drive pinions in a counter-clockwise direction, which drives the differential and final drive carrier assembly clockwise. This rotation results in a clockwise rotation of the output (axle) shafts.

DRIVE RANGE-SECOND GEAR

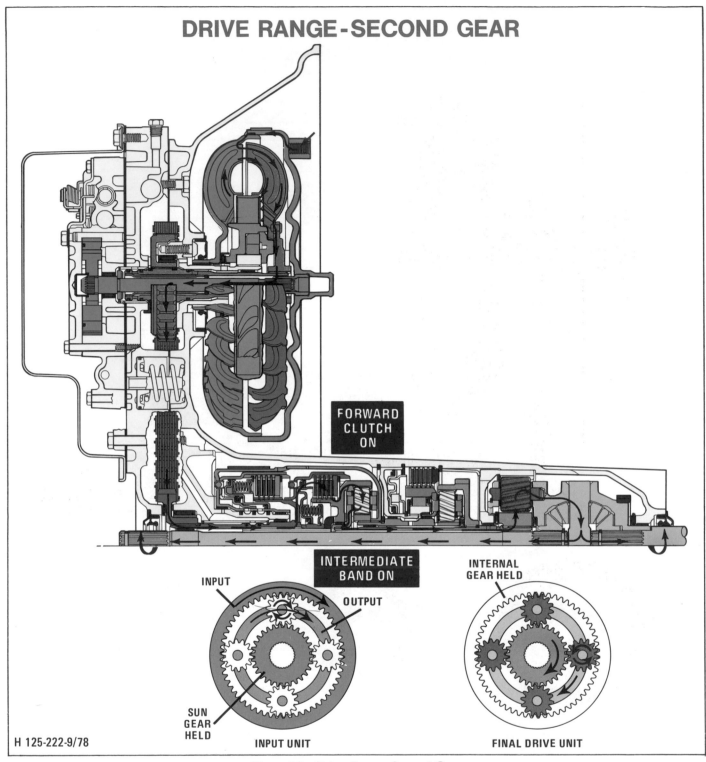

Figure 29 - Drive Range—Second Gear

FORWARD CLUTCH—APPLIED

In second gear, the intermediate band is applied to hold the sun gear from rotating. Converter torque through the forward clutch is applied to the input internal gear in a clockwise direction. Clockwise rotation of the input internal gear turns the input pinions clockwise around the stationary sun gear and causes the input carrier and final drive sun gear shaft to turn clockwise in a reduction ratio of approximately 1.60:1.

INTERMEDIATE BAND—APPLIED

The final drive sun gear shaft drives the final drive pinions in a counter-clockwise direction, which drives the differential and final drive carrier assembly clockwise. This rotation results in a clockwise rotation of the output (axle) shafts.

26

DRIVE RANGE-THIRD GEAR

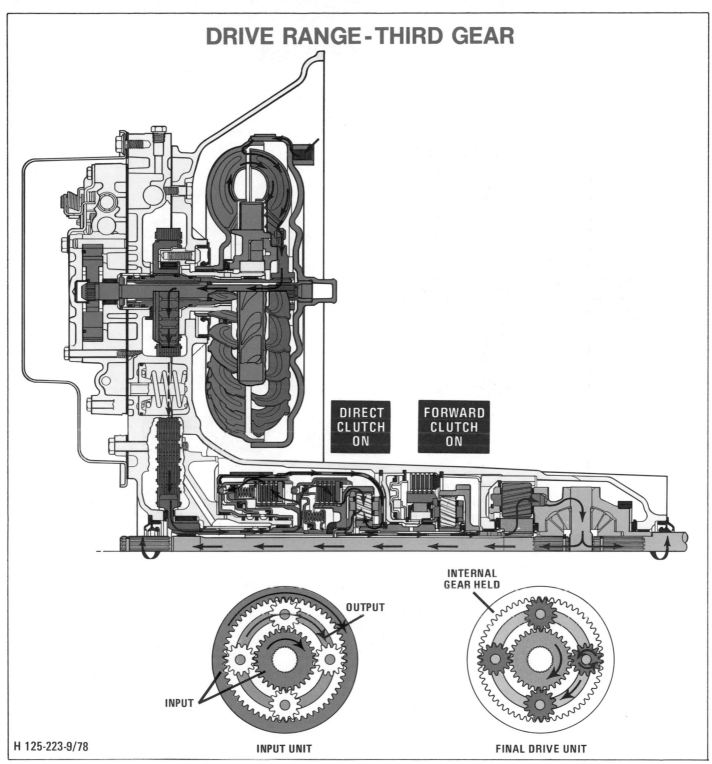

H 125-223-9/78

INPUT UNIT

FINAL DRIVE UNIT

Figure 30 - Drive Range—Third Gear

DIRECT CLUTCH—APPLIED

FORWARD CLUTCH—APPLIED

In third gear, converter torque is transmitted through the forward clutch to the input internal gear in a clockwise rotation. The direct clutch is applied and clockwise rotation is transmitted through the direct clutch to the input drum and sun gear. Since both the sun gear and input internal gear are now turning at the same speed, the planetary gear set is essentially locked and turns as one unit in direct

drive or at a ratio of 1:1. This drives the final drive sun gear shaft in a clockwise direction.

The final drive sun gear shaft drives the final drive pinions in a counter-clockwise direction which drives the differential and final drive carrier assembly clockwise. This rotation results in a clockwise rotation of the output (axle) shafts.

REVERSE

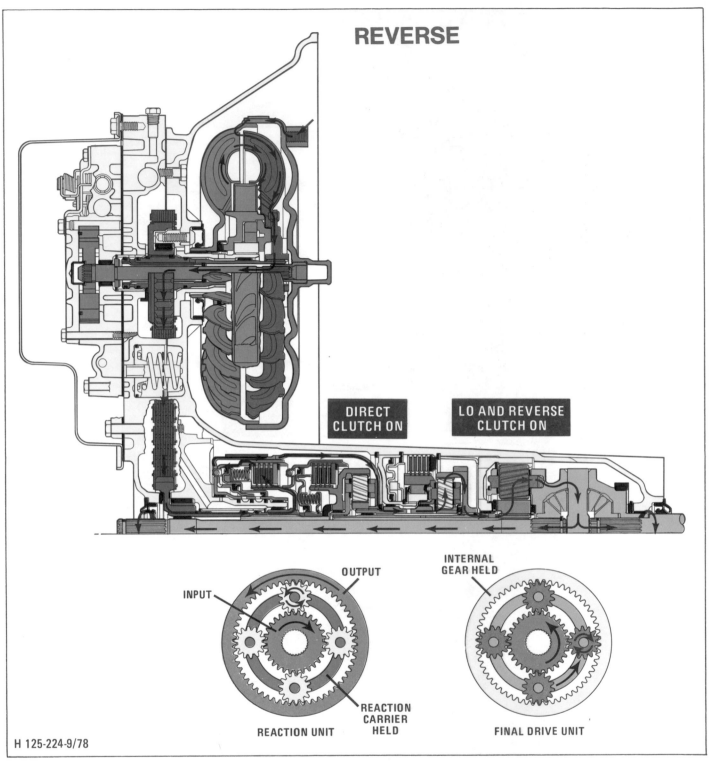

DIRECT CLUTCH ON

LO AND REVERSE CLUTCH ON

INTERNAL GEAR HELD

INPUT

OUTPUT

REACTION CARRIER HELD

REACTION UNIT

FINAL DRIVE UNIT

Figure 31 - Reverse

DIRECT CLUTCH—APPLIED

LO AND REVERSE CLUTCH—APPLIED

In Reverse, the direct clutch is applied. This delivers converter torque, through both the drive link assembly and the forward clutch housing to the input drum and sun gear. The lo and reverse clutch is applied; this prevents the reaction carrier from turning clockwise.

Clockwise torque to the sun gear causes the reaction pinions and reaction internal gear to turn counter-clockwise in reduction.

The reaction internal gear is connected directly to

the final drive sun gear shaft, thus providing the reverse output gear ratio of approximately 2.07:1. The final drive sun gear shaft drives the final drive pinions in a clockwise direction, which drives the differential and final drive carrier assembly counter-clockwise. This rotation results in counter-clockwise rotation of the output (axle) shafts.

The reverse torque multiplication at stall (converter and gear ratios) is approximately 4.04:1.

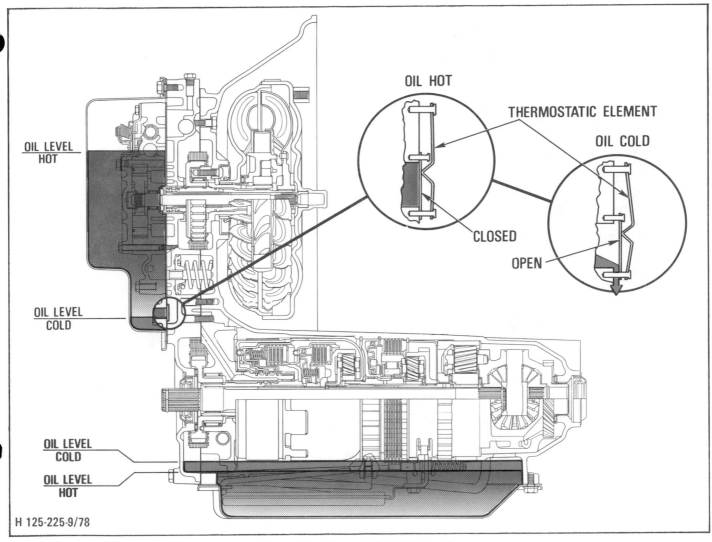

OIL HOT

THERMOSTATIC ELEMENT

OIL COLD

OIL LEVEL HOT

CLOSED

OPEN

OIL LEVEL COLD

OIL LEVEL COLD

OIL LEVEL HOT

H 125-225-9/78

Figure 33 - Hot and Cold Oil Levels

HYDRAULIC SYSTEM

In previous sections, the mechanical phase of the transmission operation has been described including references to the clutches and a band being hydraulically applied. The next section describes in detail, the hydraulic system that applies the band and clutches and controls automatic shifting.

The hydraulic pressure system requires a supply of transmission fluid. Due to the low profile of the THM 125, a reservoir area other than the oil pan is required to operate the unit with both hot and cold fluid level. The fluid level in this reservoir, located in the lower section of the valve body cover, is controlled by a thermostatic element (Fig. 32). This element operates by opening and closing according to the temperature of the fluid that is trapped in the reservoir portion of the valve body cover. As the temperature of the fluid in the reservoir increases, the volume of the fluid increases. As the temperature decreases, the thermostatic element opens and lets the fluid drain into the lower sump or oil pan (Fig. 33).

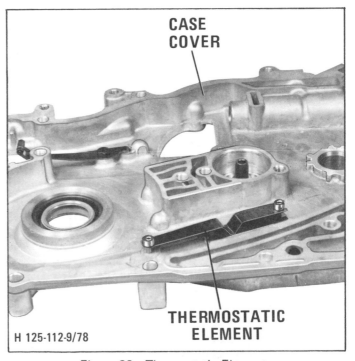

CASE COVER

THERMOSTATIC ELEMENT

H 125-112-9/78

Figure 32 - Thermostatic Element

29

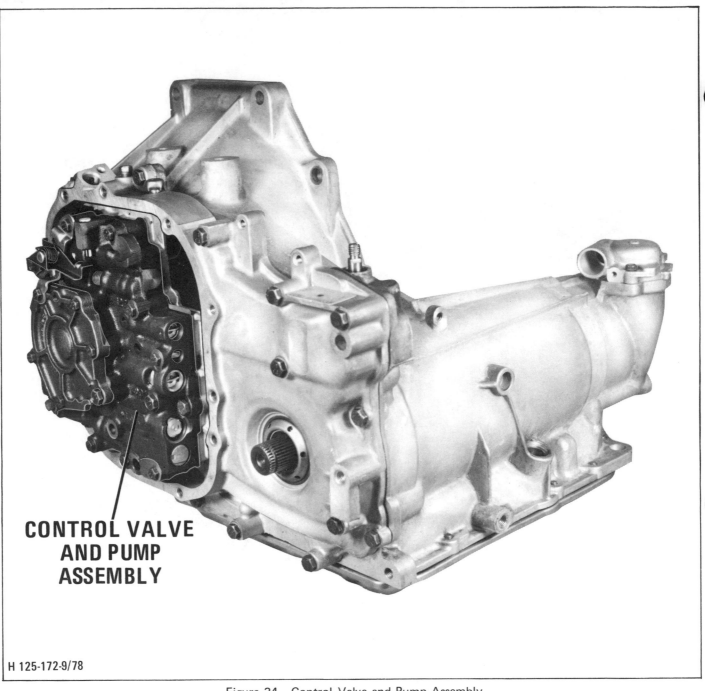

CONTROL VALVE AND PUMP ASSEMBLY

H 125-172-9/78

Figure 34 - Control Valve and Pump Assembly

PUMP ASSEMBLY

The oil pump is a variable capacity vane type pump driven by the engine. It is located with-in the transmission control valve and pump assembly (Fig. 34). A slide is incorporated in the pump that automatically regulates pump output, according to the needs of the transmission. Maximum pump output is obtained when the priming spring has been fully extended and has the slide held against the side of the body (Fig. 35). As the slide moves toward the center, the pump output is reduced until minimum output is reached.

PRESSURE REGULATOR

Movement of the slide is accomplished by directing oil from the pressure regulator to the pump side opposite the priming spring. With the engine off, the pump is at rest and the slide is held opposite by the force of the priming spring. As the pump rotor operates, its output is directed to the pressure regulator valve. When output is below the desired pressure, the pressure regulator valve is held deep in its bore by the pressure regulator valve spring. With the pressure regulator valve in this position, the slide is held by the priming spring for maximum output. As the pump output and pressure in the system increases, the pressure regulator valve is moved outward, directing oil to move the slide compressing the priming spring and decreasing the pump output (Fig. 36).

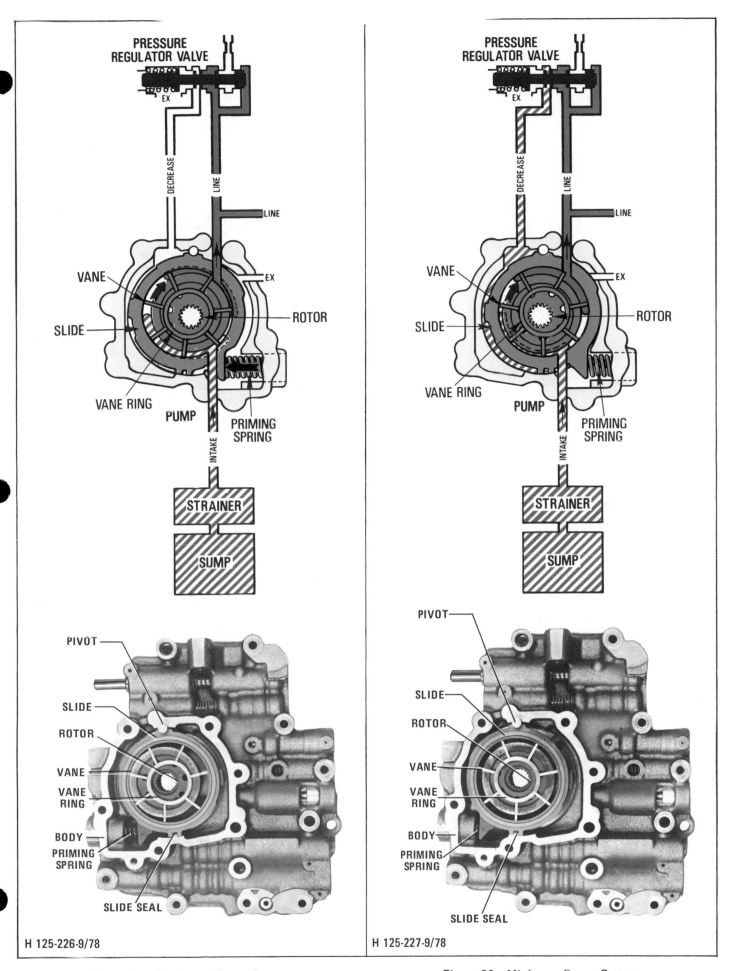

Figure 35 - Maximum Pump Output

Figure 36 - Minimum Pump Output

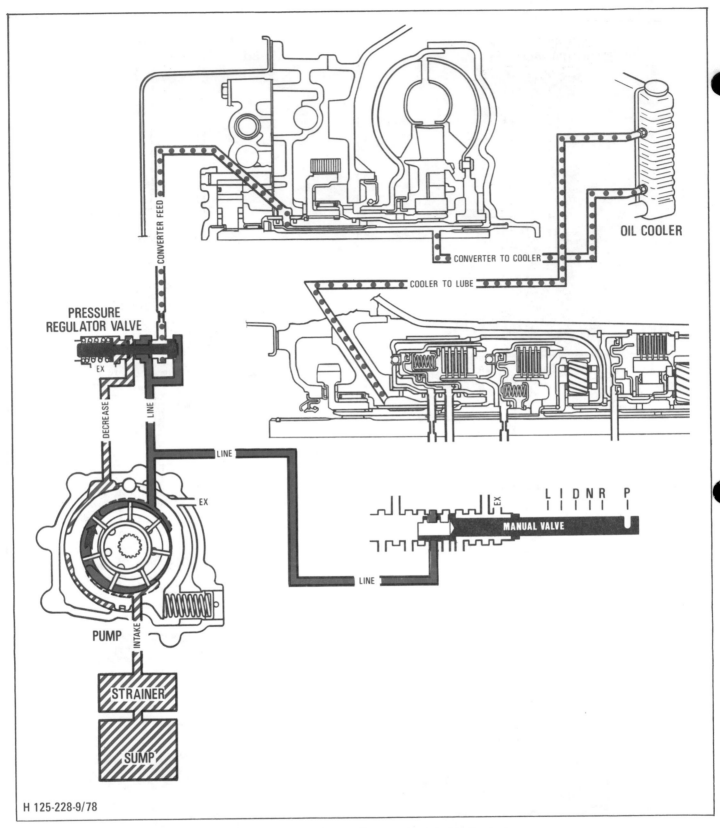

Figure 37 - Oil Pump and Pressure Regulating System

Oil from the pressure regulator is also directed to fill the converter. When the converter is filled, oil returning from the converter is directed to the transmission cooler in the radiator. Oil returning from the cooler is then directed to the transmission lubrication system (Fig. 37).

The requirements of the transmission for apply of the band and clutches vary with engine torque and throttle opening. Under heavy throttle operation the 482 kPa (70 psi) line pressure is not sufficient to hold the band and clutches on without slipping. To provide higher line pressure with greater throttle opening, a variable oil pressure related to throttle opening is desired.

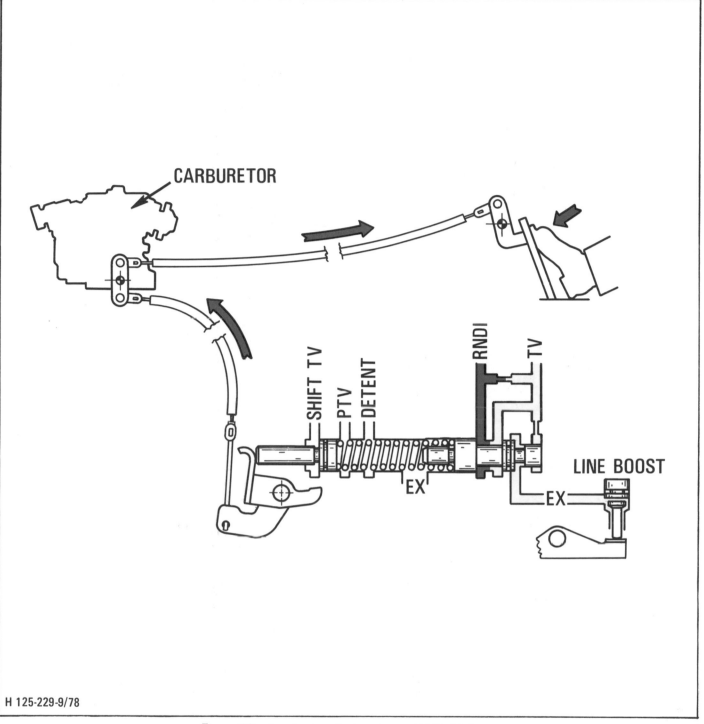

Figure 38 - Accelerator, Carburetor and T.V. Linkage

THROTTLE VALVE

Throttle valve (T.V.) pressure is related to carburetor opening which is related to engine torque. As the accelerator pedal is depressed and the carburetor opened, the mechanical linkage (T.V. cable) relays the movement to the throttle plunger and increases the force on the T.V. spring and throttle valve, increasing T.V. pressure. T.V. pressure can regulate from 0 to approximately 723 kPa (105 psi) (Fig. 38).

Notice: The throttle valve is fed by RNDI (reverse, neutral, drive and intermediate) oil. There is no T.V. pressure in Park or Lo range.

33

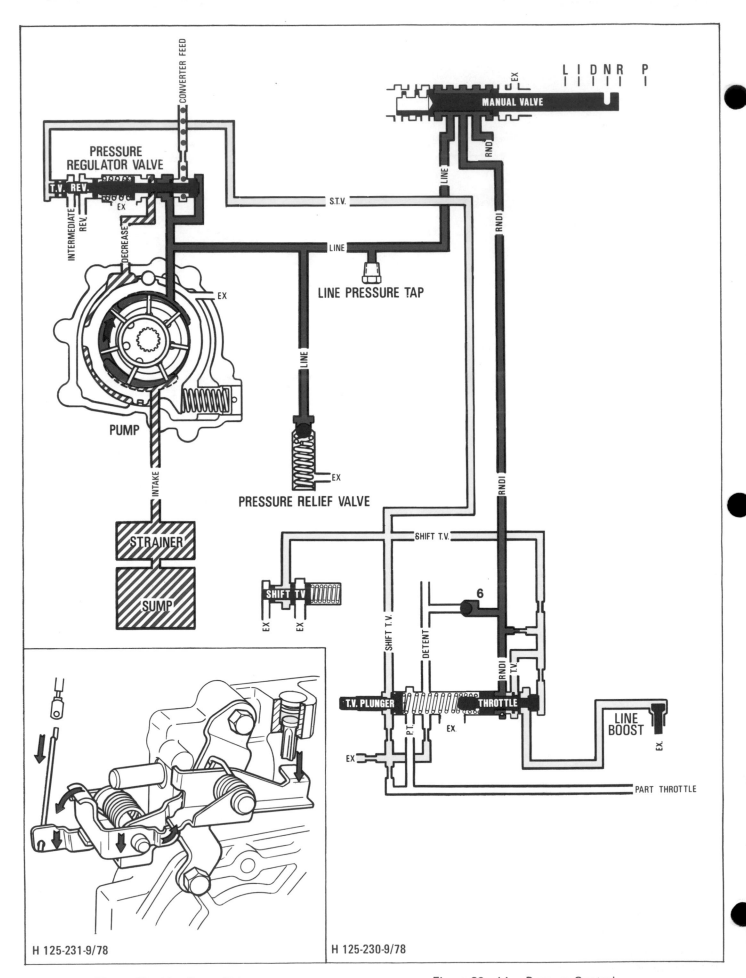

Figure 40 - Line Boost Valve

Figure 39 - Line Pressure Control

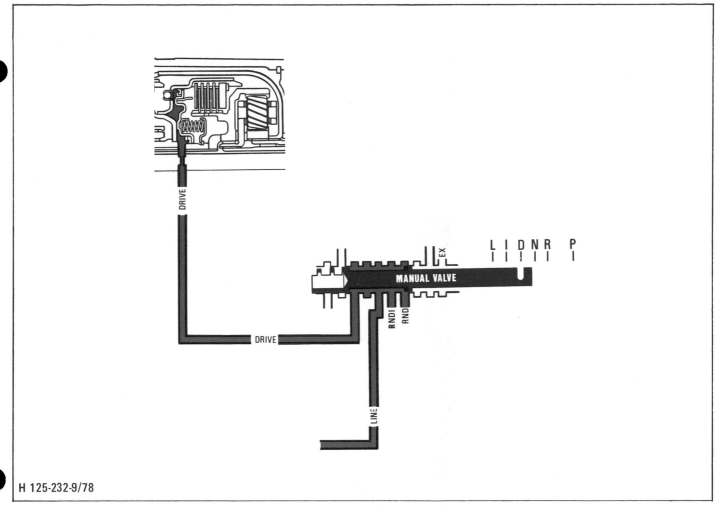

Figure 41 - Forward Clutch Applied

SHIFT T.V. VALVE

It is desirable, for shift control, to limit T.V. pressure to a maximum of 620 kPa (90 psi). This is accomplished by routing T.V. pressure through an orifice to the shift T.V. valve. The shift T.V. valve will exhaust any oil over 620 kPa (90 psi) (Fig. 39).

Shift T.V. oil is directed to the T.V. plunger to provide a hydraulic assist to reduce accelerator pedal effort necessary to actuate the plunger. Shift T.V. oil is also directed to the T.V. boost valve, which will boost line pressure according to throttle opening from 482 kPa to 965 kPa, (70 psi to 140 psi).

To maintain stable pressure, there are orifices (slots) in the control valve and pump assembly, spacer plate, and spacer plate gaskets that let any air in the system exhaust.

LINE BOOST VALVE

A feature has been included in the T.V. system that will prevent the transmission from being operated with low or minimum line pressure in the event the T.V. cable is disconnected or broken. This feature is the line boost valve which is located in the control valve and pump assembly at the T.V. regulating exhaust port.

The line boost valve is held off its seat by the throttle lever and bracket assembly, (this allows T.V. oil to regulate normally), when the T.V. cable is properly adjusted. If the T.V. cable becomes disconnected or is not adjusted properly, the line boost valve will close the T.V. exhaust port and keep T.V. and line pressure at full line pressure (Fig. 40).

FORWARD CLUTCH

When the transmission selector lever is moved to the Drive position, the manual valve moves to allow line pressure to be delivered to the forward clutch (Fig. 41). The oil is metered to the forward clutch piston through an orifice to provide a smooth apply of the clutch.

With the forward clutch applied, a mechanical connection has been provided between the input shaft and the input internal gear. The roller clutch assembly becomes effective as a result of the power flow through the compound planetary gear set; thus the transmission is in first gear, ready for the vehicle to start moving.

As the vehicle begins to accelerate and first gear reduction is no longer required, the transmission automatically shifts to second gear.

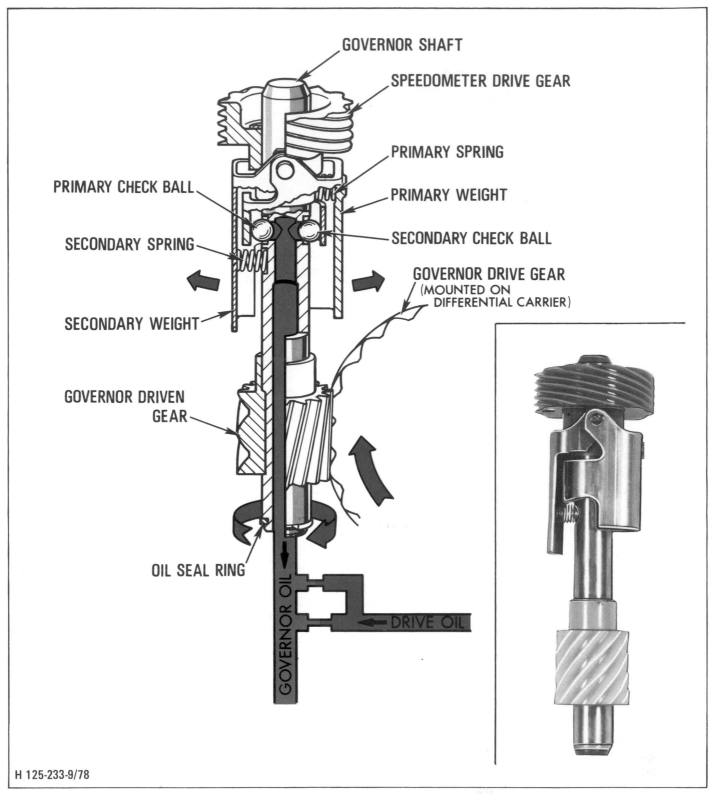

GOVERNOR SHAFT

SPEEDOMETER DRIVE GEAR

PRIMARY SPRING

PRIMARY CHECK BALL

PRIMARY WEIGHT

SECONDARY CHECK BALL

SECONDARY SPRING

SECONDARY WEIGHT

GOVERNOR DRIVE GEAR
(MOUNTED ON
DIFFERENTIAL CARRIER)

GOVERNOR DRIVEN
GEAR

OIL SEAL RING

GOVERNOR OIL

DRIVE OIL

H 125-233-9/78

Figure 42 - Governor Assembly

GOVERNOR ASSEMBLY

The vehicle speed signal for the shift is supplied by the transmission governor which is driven by the differential and final drive carrier (Fig. 42). The governor assembly consists of a governor shaft, a driven gear, two check balls, a primary weight, a secondary weight, primary and secondary spring, one governor weight pin and an oil seal ring. The check balls seat in two pockets directly opposite each other in the governor shaft. The weights are so arranged that the primary weight, assisted by the primary spring, acts on one check ball and the secondary weight, assisted by the secondary spring, acts on the other check ball. As the governor turns, the weights are moved outward by the centrifugal force. This force is relayed to the check balls, seating them; and as the speed of the governor increases, so does the force relayed to the check balls.

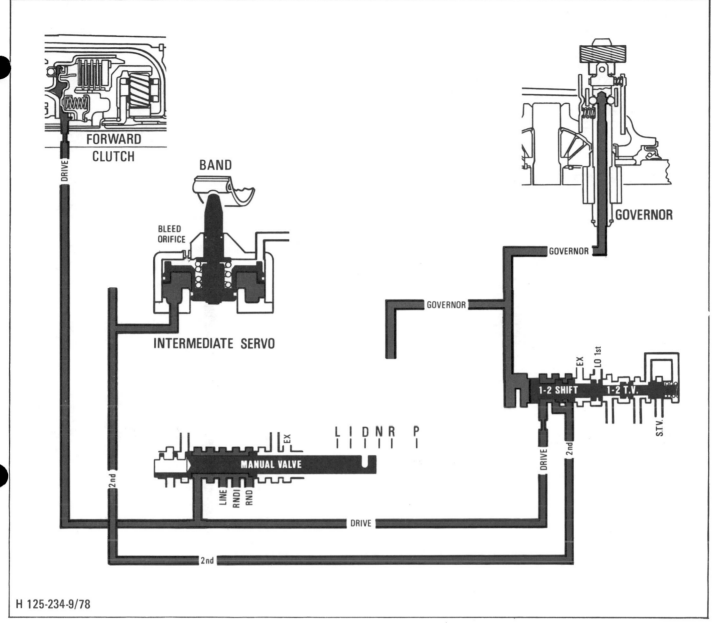

Figure 43 - 1-2 Shift

H 125-234-9/78

Drive oil pressure is metered through two orifices to feed the governor and acts on the check balls, tending to open them for exhaust. Centrifugal force acting on the check balls, through the governor weights, tends to seat the check balls and seal the exhaust.

The heavier or primary weight and spring are more sensitive to changes in differential and final drive carrier speeds at lower rpm than the secondary weight. At greater vehicle speeds as centrifugal force increases on the primary weight, it finally holds its check ball seated and no longer exhausts any oil. From this point on the secondary weight and spring are used to apply force to their respective check ball and regulate the exhausting of drive oil pressure.

The exhausting of the drive oil feeding the governor is regulated by the forces on the check balls; and when the forces are balanced, the oil pressure remaining is at variable governor pressure, which is proportional to vehicle speed.

With the governor not rotating, there is no centrifugal force and all of the oil is exhausted, leaving no governor pressure. Governor oil pressure increases with vehicle and governor speed; and at some governor speed, both check balls are held closed, thus governor pressure will equal drive oil pressure.

1-2 SHIFT VALVE

The 1-2 shift valve train is used to make the shift from first to second gear (Fig. 43). A spring acting on the 1-2 valve train tends to keep it in the closed position, blocking drive oil. Governor pressure is directed to the 1-2 shift valve to act against the spring force. As the vehicle speed is increased, governor pressure increases, overcoming the spring force; and the 1-2 valve train opens, allowing drive oil to flow to the intermediate servo to apply the intermediate band; thus the transmission has shifted to second gear.

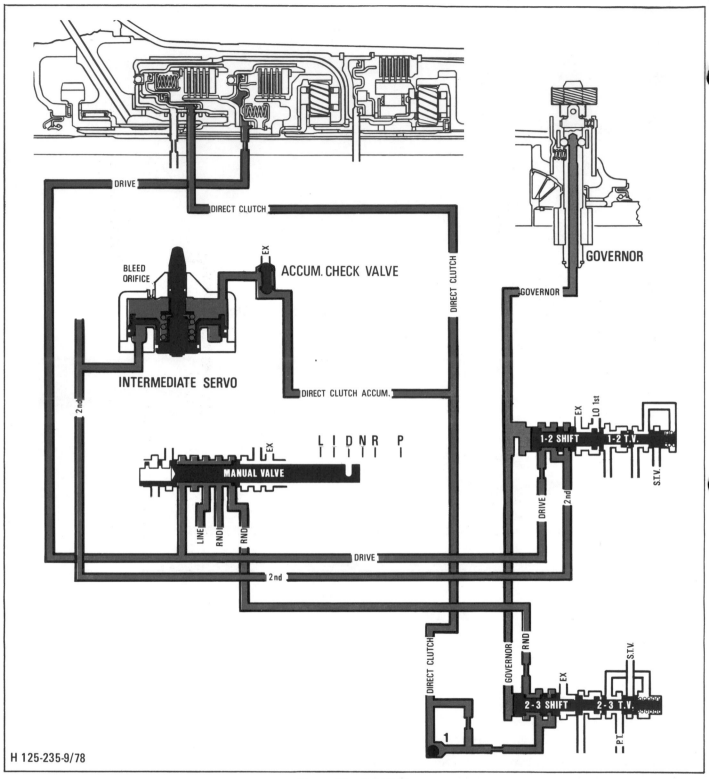

Figure 44 - 2-3 Shift

2-3 SHIFT VALVE

Further increases in vehicle speed and governor pressure will cause the transmission to shift to third gear. The shift to third gear is initiated by the 2-3 shift valve train (Fig. 44). The operation of the 2-3 shift valve train is very similiar to the 1-2 shift valve train. A spring acting on the shift valve train tends to keep the valve closed, blocking reverse, neutral and drive (RND) oil coming from the manual valve, while governor pressure attempts to open the valve. When vehicle speed increases enough to develop sufficient governor pressure to open the 2-3 shift valve train, RND oil passes through an orifice to the shift valve and enters the direct clutch passage. Direct clutch oil is routed to apply the direct clutch. It also seats the accumulator check valve and goes to the release side of the intermediate servo piston to release the band, thus shifting the transmission into third gear. The direct clutch piston has two apply areas and oil pressure is applied to only the smaller, inner area in third gear.

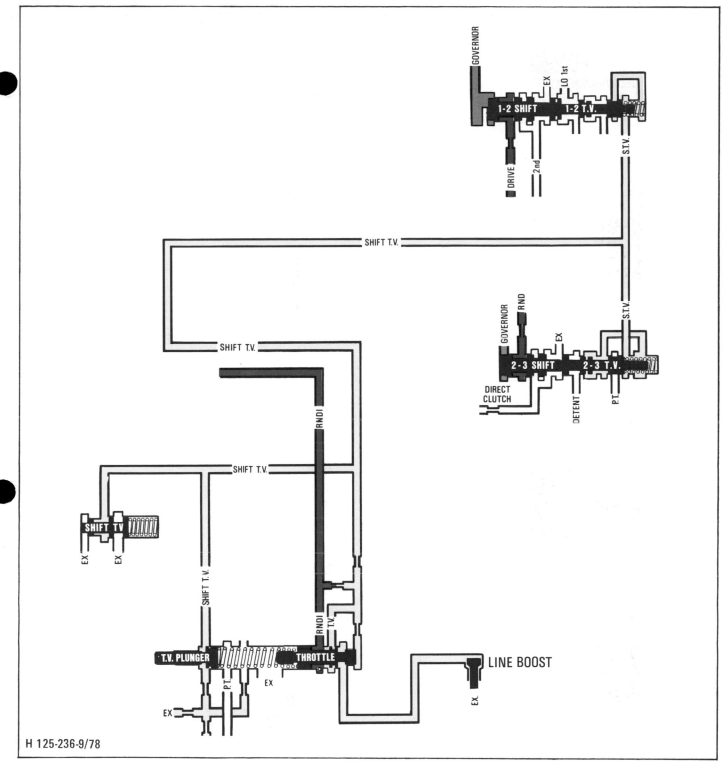

Figure 45 - Shift T.V. Pressure

SHIFT T.V. PRESSURE

The 1-2 and 2-3 shifts will always take place at the same vehicle speeds (in the system as described); that is, whenever the governor pressure overcomes the force of the springs on the shift valves. When accelerating under a heavy load or for maximum performance, it is desirable to have the shifts occur at higher vehicle speeds.

Shift T.V. pressure is used to make the transmission shift at higher vehicle speeds with greater throttle openings (Fig. 45). Shift T.V. pressure, which increases with throttle opening, is directed to the 1-2 and 2-3 throttle valves assisting the springs to hold the shift valves in the closed position. Governor pressure must now overcome shift T.V. pressure, plus the spring force to open the 1-2 and 2-3 shift valves. The shifts can now be delayed to take place at higher vehicle speeds with heavier throttle operation.

39

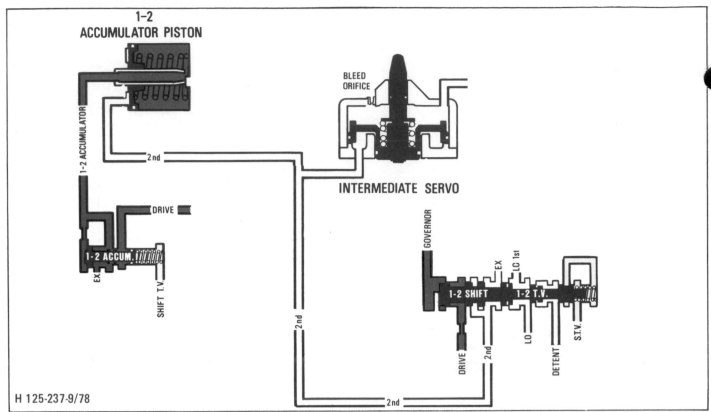

Figure 46 - 1-2 Accumulator and Intermediate Servo—First Gear

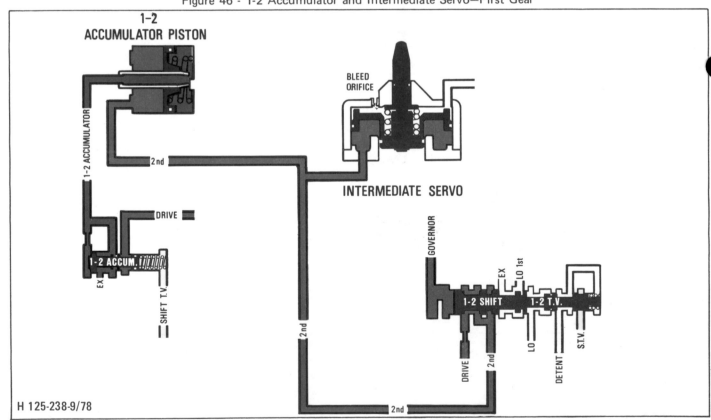

Figure 47 - 1-2 Accumulator and Intermediate Servo—Second Gear

1-2 ACCUMULATOR VALVE

The 1-2 shift feel and the durability of the intermediate band are largely dependent on the pressure that applies the band. At minimum or light throttle operation, the engine develops a small amount of torque; and as a result, the band requires less apply force to hold the direct clutch housing. At heavy throttle, the engine develops a large amount of torque which requires a greater apply pressure to lock the band on the direct clutch housing. If the band locks too quickly, the shift will be too aggressive. If it locks too slowly, it will slip excessively and burn due to the heat created by the slippage.

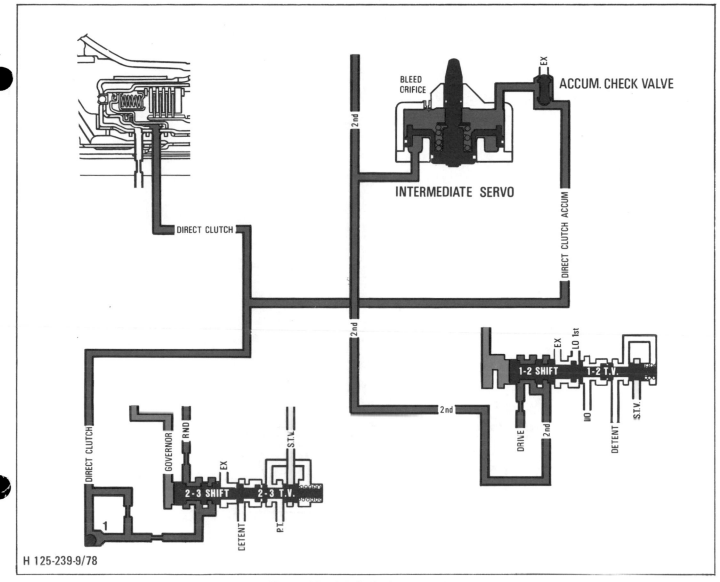

Figure 48 - 2-3 Shift Accumulation

Controlling of the intermediate band apply pressure is accomplished by a 1-2 accumulator valve which provides a variable accumulator pressure to cushion the band apply in relation to throttle opening (Fig. 46).

The 1-2 accumulator valve system is supplied by drive oil pressure and is controlled by shift T.V. pressure. For light throttle operation, drive oil is regulated to a lesser 1-2 accumulator pressure. At heavy throttle, 1-2 accumulator pressure is increased by shift T.V. pressure. 1-2 accumulator pressure is supplied to act on one side of the 1-2 accumulator piston located in the case cover assembly. In first gear, 1-2 accumulator pressure is directed to the 1-2 accumulator piston to make it ready for the 1-2 shift.

When the 1-2 shift valve opens, second oil strokes the intermediate servo piston (Fig. 47), compressing the servo cushion spring and applying the intermediate band. Second oil is also directed to the 1-2 accumulator piston and strokes the 1-2 accumulator piston against 1-2 accumulator pressure and the 1-2 accumulator spring. This action absorbs some intermediate band apply (second) oil and permits the band apply time and pressure to be controlled for proper shift feel.

2-3 SHIFT ACCUMULATION

The direct clutch apply rate is controlled by the intermediate servo piston (Fig. 48). In second gear, the servo piston is stroked by second oil, compressing the cushion spring and applying the intermediate band. Second oil varies with line pressure, thus the pressure on the intermediate servo piston is varied according to throttle opening.

When the 2-3 shift valve opens, direct clutch oil flows to the direct clutch, and seats accumulator check valve to the release side of the intermediate servo piston. The servo cushion spring force and direct clutch accumulator oil pressure will overcome the pressure of the second oil and move the servo piston to release the band. The stroking of the servo piston to release the band acts as an accumulator and absorbs some direct clutch oil. This permits the direct clutch to apply at a controlled rate for a smooth 2-3 shift.

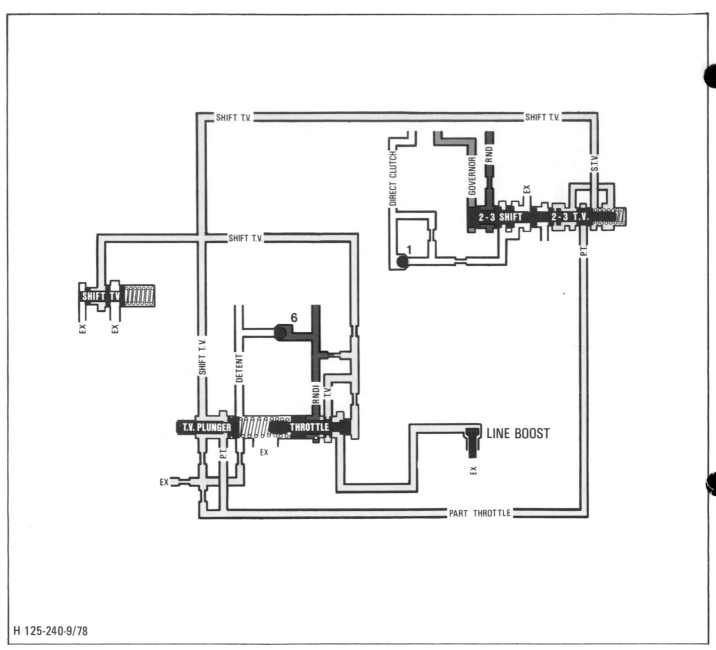

Figure 49 - 3-2 Downshift Timing, Coast Down and Part Throttle

H 125-240-9/78

PART THROTTLE 3-2 DOWNSHIFT

During moderate acceleration at low speeds in third gear, the torque converter provides additional torque multiplication for improved performance. For more performance with additional throttle opening, the THM 125 transmission has a part throttle 3-2 downshift (Fig. 49).

A part throttle 3-2 downshift can be accomplished at speeds below approximately 50 mph (80 km/h) by depressing the accelerator pedal far enough to move the T.V. plunger to open the part throttle (P.T.) passage. The travel of the T.V. plunger raises shift T.V. pressure and allows shift T.V. oil into the P.T. passage to act on the 2-3 throttle valve. This oil moves the 2-3 valve train against governor pressure and shifts the transmission to second gear.

DETENT (FULL THROTTLE) 3-2 DOWNSHIFT

At speeds below approximately 65 mph (105 km/h), a 3-2 detent downshift can be obtained by fully depressing the accelerator pedal (Fig. 50). This will move the T.V. plunger to provide full T.V. pressure and open up the detent passage in addition to the P.T. passage. Shift T.V. oil is now directed into the detent passage as well as the P.T. passage and to the 2-3 throttle valve. Shift T.V. oil and detent oil acting on two areas on the 2-3 throttle valve will move the 2-3 shift valve against governor pressure, shifting the transmission to second gear.

A detent 2-1 downshift can also be accomplished below approximately 30 mph (48 km/h) because detent oil is directed to the 1-2 throttle valve (Fig. 50). Detent oil and shift T.V. oil acting on the 1-2 throttle valve moves the 1-2 shift valve against governor pressure, shifting the transmission to first gear.

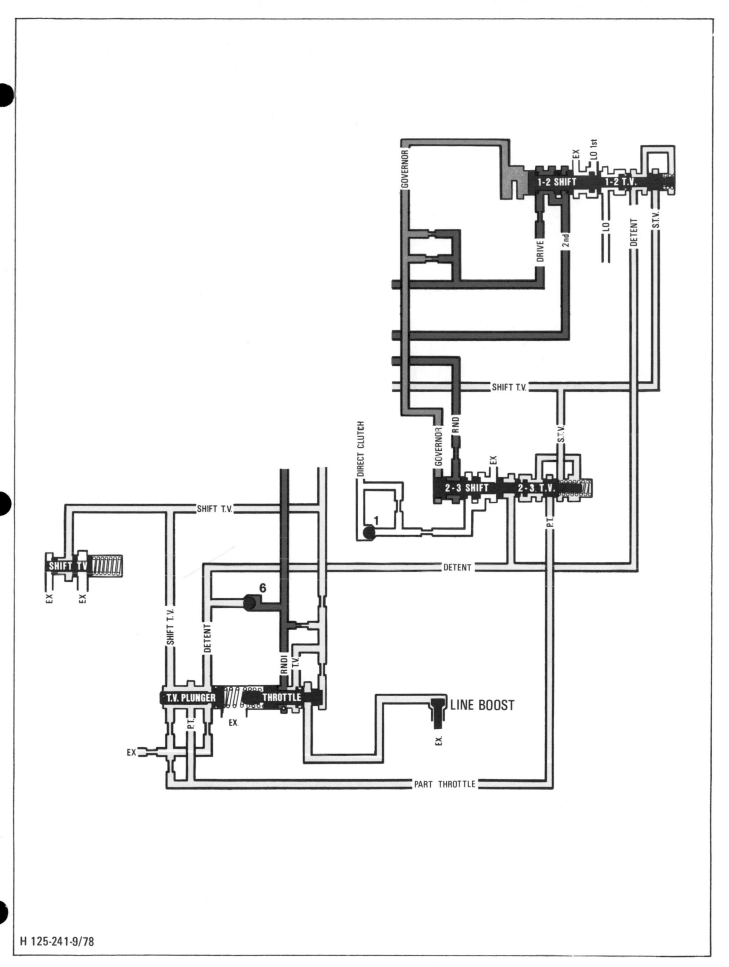

Figure 50 - Detent (Full Throttle) Downshift 3-2, Valves in Second Gear Position

H 125-241-9/78

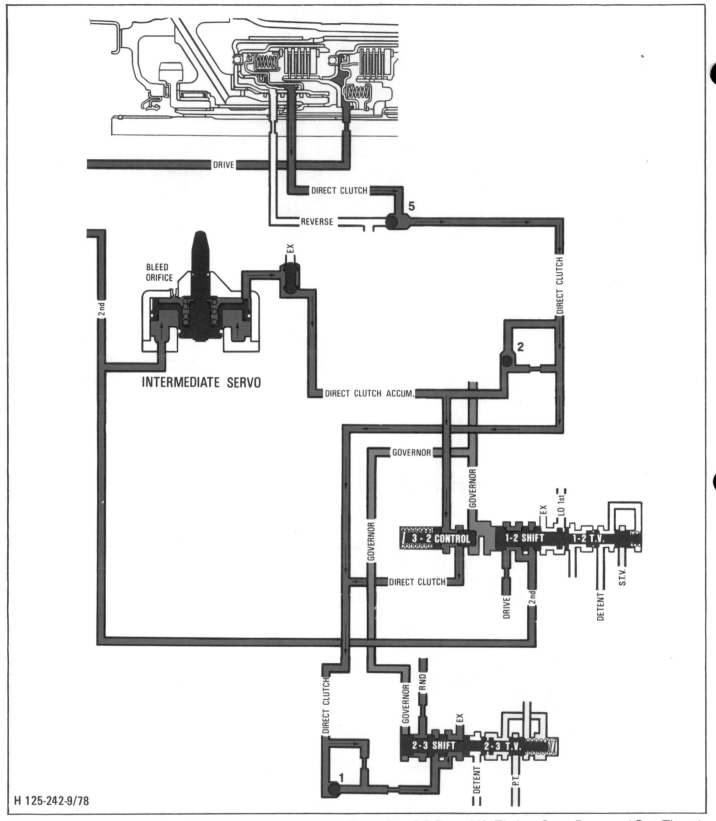

3-2 DOWNSHIFT TIMING

Figure 51 - 3-2 Downshift Timing, Coast Down and Part Throttle

The rate at which the direct clutch releases and the intermediate band applies during forced 3-2 downshifts is controlled by the 3-2 control valve.

During part throttle downshifts below approximately 50 mph (80 km/h), the exhausting direct clutch apply oil and direct clutch accumulator oil is regulated by the 3-2 control valve according to car speed.

This regulated exhaust oil seats the direct clutch exhaust check ball (1) and flows through two orifices, exhausting at the 2-3 shift valve. This allows the direct clutch to release gradually at the same time second oil applies the intermediate band (Fig. 51).

On detent 3-2 downshifts, above approximately 50 mph (80 km/h), it is desirable to have the direct clutch re-

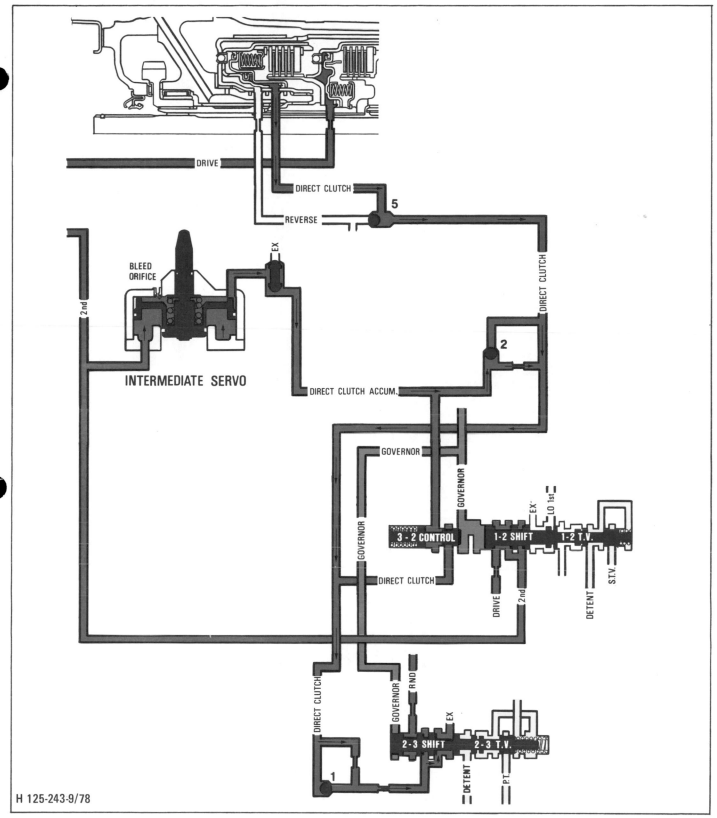

Figure 52 - 3-2 Detent Downshift Timing

lease quickly as the intermediate band applies. This allows the engine rpm to increase at the proper rate for a smooth transfer of the driving load to the intermediate band. Governor pressure will move the 3-2 control valve which blocks direct clutch accumulator oil from flowing through the valve. Exhausting direct clutch oil still seats the direct clutch exhaust check ball (1), and flows through the two orifices, exhausting at the 2-3 shift valve. The exhausting direct clutch accumulator oil seats the direct clutch accumulator check ball (2) and flows through another orifice, controlling the apply of the intermediate band (Fig 52), before following the same path as the exhausting direct clutch oil.

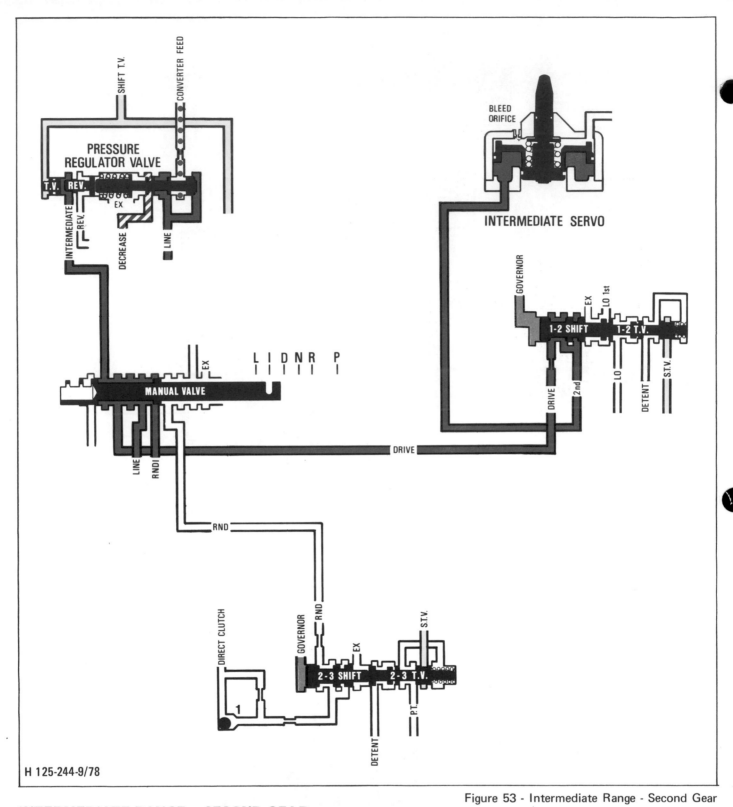

H 125-244-9/78

Figure 53 - Intermediate Range - Second Gear

INTERMEDIATE RANGE — SECOND GEAR

When the selector lever is moved to Intermediate range position, the manual valve is moved to block off the supply of RND oil to the 2-3 shift valve and opens an exhaust port for the RND oil that was applying the direct clutch and releasing the intermediate band (Fig. 53). Second oil applies the intermediate band; and with the direct clutch released, the transmission has now shifted to second gear. With the RND oil blocked at the manual valve, the transmission will downshift to second gear regardless of speed.

Intermediate oil is directed from the manual valve to the reverse boost valve. Intermediate oil acting on the reverse boost valve, plus the pressure regulator spring, will boost line pressure to 827 kPa (120 psi). This pressure provides sufficient holding force on the band for closed throttle overrun engine braking.

46

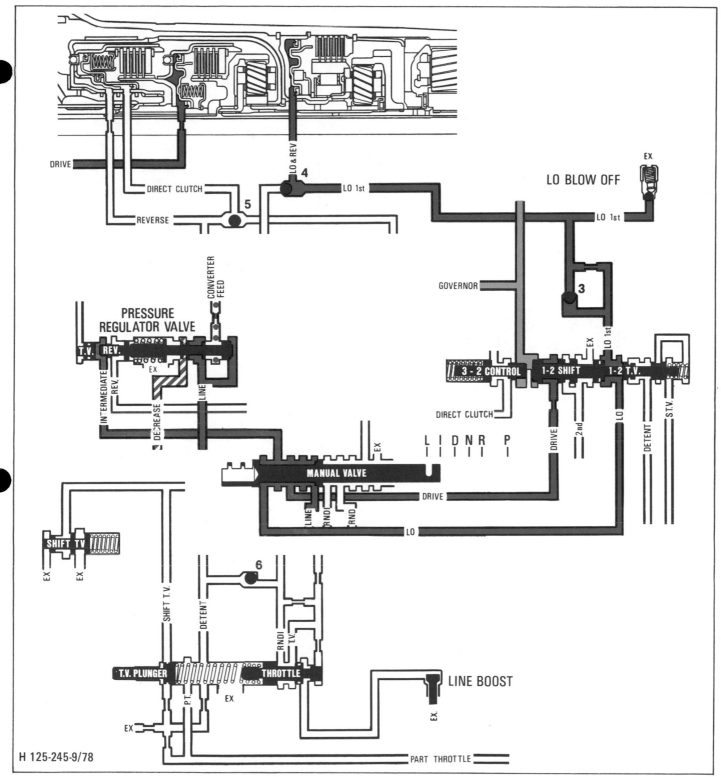

Figure 54 - Lo Range - First Gear

LO RANGE — FIRST GEAR

Moving the selector lever to Lo range, positions the manual valve to open a passage directing lo oil to the 1-2 throttle valve. Lo oil pressure, is the same as intermediate oil pressure 827 kPa (120 psi), because intermediate oil is still present. Lo oil pressure and the 1-2 T.V. spring will close the 1-2 shift valve at speeds below approximately 40 mph (64 km/h). This allows lo oil to enter the lo 1st passage. Lo 1st oil seats lo 1st check ball (3) and passes through an orifice to the lo blow off valve. This lo blow off valve exhausts lo 1st oil down to 241 kPa (35 psi). This re-regulated oil is then directed to seat the lo and reverse check ball (4) and to the lo and reverse clutch for a smooth apply (Fig. 54).

The RNDI and detent check ball (6) is located between RNDI and detent oil passages (Fig. 54). This check ball is there to prevent the transmission from being tricked into lo range above the lo range lockout point.

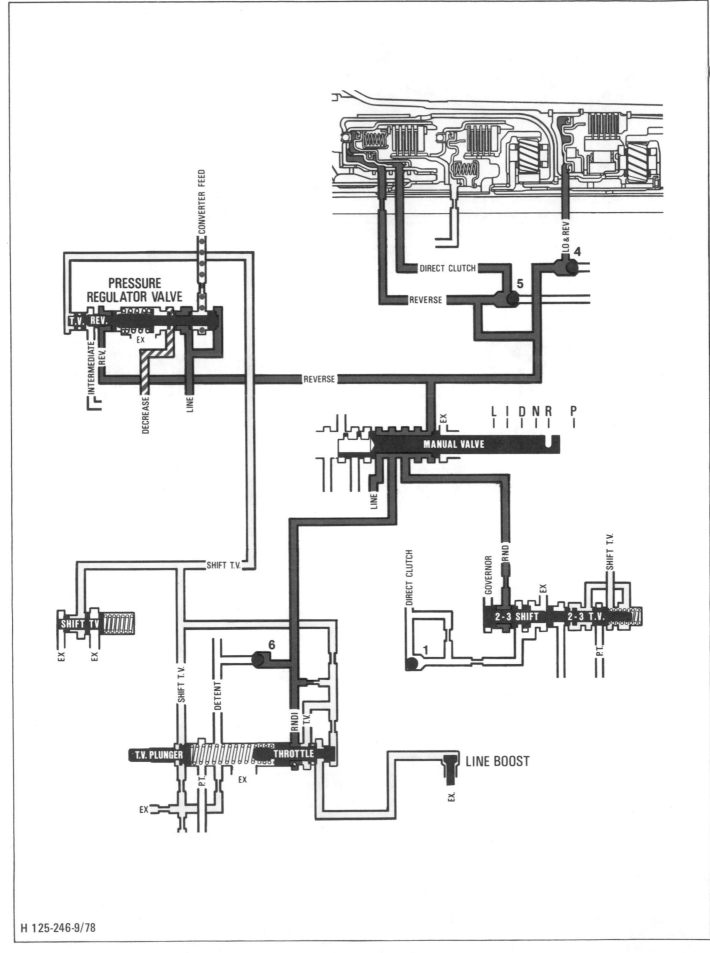

Figure 55 - Reverse

H 125-246-9/78

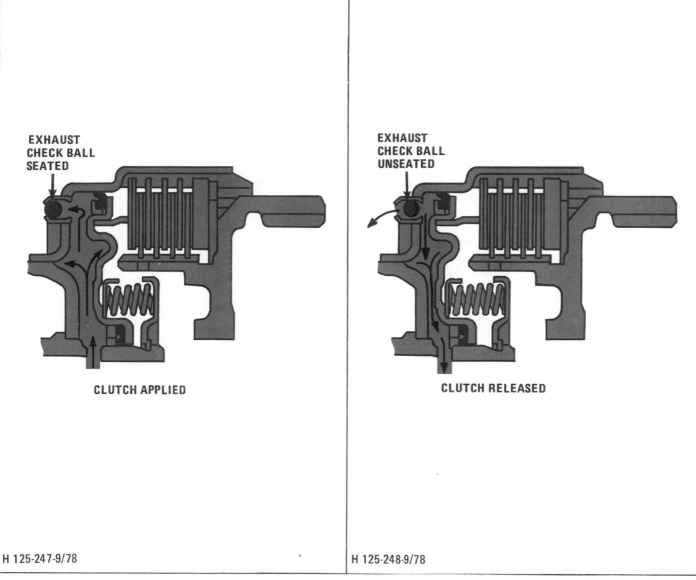

EXHAUST CHECK BALL SEATED

CLUTCH APPLIED

H 125-247-9/78

EXHAUST CHECK BALL UNSEATED

CLUTCH RELEASED

H 125-248-9/78

Figure 56 - Exhaust Check Ball Applied

Figure 57 - Exhaust Check Ball Release

REVERSE

Selecting the Reverse position, moves the manual valve to allow drive, intermediate and lo oil to be exhausted. Line oil then enters the reverse passage where it seats the lo and reverse check ball (4) in the lo 1st passage and applies the lo and reverse clutch (Fig. 55).

Reverse oil is also directed to the direct clutch and reverse check ball (5) seating it in the direct clutch passage. This oil is then directed to the inner, smaller area of the direct clutch. Reverse oil is also directed to the outer, larger area of the direct clutch piston through an orifice for a smooth apply of the direct clutch.

To insure adequate oil pressure for the torque requirements reverse oil acts on the reverse boost valve and this will boost reverse line pressure to about 827 kPa (120 psi).

Shift T.V. oil on the T.V. boost valve will boost reverse line pressure from 827 kPa to 1447 kPa (120 psi to 210 psi) at full throttle.

CLUTCH EXHAUST CHECK BALLS

To complete the exhaust of apply oil when the forward or direct clutch is released, an exhaust check ball assembly is installed near the outer diameter of the clutch housings.

Centrifugal force, resulting from the spinning clutch housings, working on the residual oil in the clutch piston cavity would give a partial apply of the clutch plates if it were not exhausted. The exhaust check ball assembly is designed to close the exhaust port by clutch apply pressure seating the check ball when the clutch is being applied (Fig. 56).

When the clutch is released and clutch apply oil is being exhausted, centrifugal force on the check ball unseats it and opens the port to exhaust the residual oil from the clutch piston cavity (Fig. 57).

TYPICAL 125 CONTROL VALVE ASSEMBLY

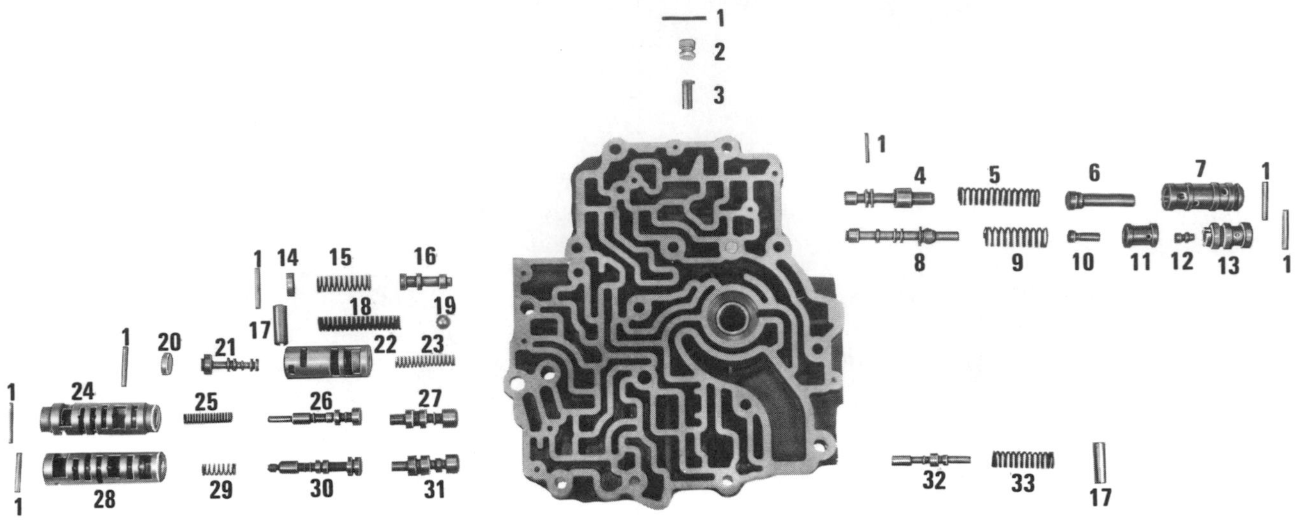

H 125-249-9/78

1. RETAINING COILED PIN
2. LINE BOOST VALVE PLUG
3. LINE BOOST VALVE
4. THROTTLE VALVE
5. THROTTLE VALVE SPRING
6. THROTTLE VALVE PLUNGER
7. T.V. PLUNGER BUSHING
8. PRESSURE REGULATOR VALVE
9. PRESSURE REGULATOR SPRING
10. REVERSE BOOST VALVE
11. REVERSE BOOST VALVE BUSHING
12. T.V. BOOST VALVE
13. T.V. BOOST VALVE BUSHING
14. VALVE BORE PLUG
15. SHIFT T.V. SPRING
16. SHIFT T.V. VALVE
17. SPRING RETAINING SLEEVE
18. PRESSURE RELIEF SPRING
19. PRESSURE RELIEF BALL
20. VALVE BORE PLUG
21. 1-2 ACCUMULATOR VALVE
22. 1-2 ACCUMULATOR BUSHING
23. 1-2 ACCUMULATOR SPRING
24. 2-3 THROTTLE VALVE BUSHING
25. 2-3 THROTTLE VALVE SPRING
26. 2-3 THROTTLE VALVE
27. 2-3 SHIFT VALVE
28. 1-2 THROTTLE VALVE BUSHING
29. 1-2 THROTTLE VALVE SPRING
30. 1-2 THROTTLE VALVE
31. 1-2 SHIFT VLAVE
32. 3-2 CONTROL VALVE
33. 3-2 VALVE SPRING
34. LO BLOW OFF BALL
35. LO BLOW OFF SPRING AND PLUG ASSEMBLY
36. LO BLOW OFF VALVE PLUG

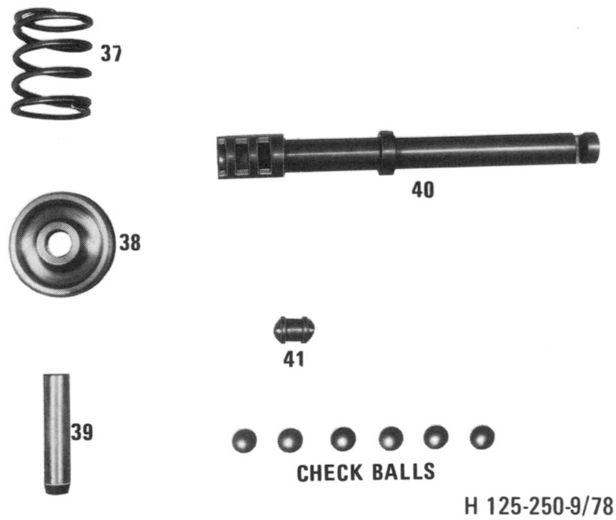

H 125-250-9/78

(Located in Case Cover)
37. 1-2 ACCUMULATOR PISTON SPRING
38. 1-2 ACCUMULATOR PISTON
39. 1-2 ACCUMULATOR PIN
40. MANUAL VALVE

(Located in Case)
41. ACCUMULATOR EXHAUST CHECK VALVE

CHECK BALLS

1. DIRECT CLUTCH EXHAUST CHECK BALL —
   (Located in Control Valve and Pump Assembly)
2. DIRECT CLUTCH ACCUMULATOR CHECK BALL —
   (Check balls 2-6 located in case cover).
3. LO 1st CHECK BALL.
4. LO AND REVERSE CHECK BALL.
5. DIRECT CLUTCH AND REVERSE CHECK BALL.
6. RNDI AND DETENT CHECK BALL.

Figure 58 - Typical THM 125 Control Valve and Pump Assembly

SUMMARY OF VALVE FUNCTION

ACCUMULATOR CHECK VALVE:
Opens or closes the exhaust port in the direct clutch accumulator passage. It exhausts oil from the release side of intermediate servo.

1-2 ACCUMULATOR VALVE:
Regulates drive oil to 1-2 accumulator piston. It is supplied by drive oil and controlled by shift T.V. oil. It produces a variable accumulator pressure to cushion intermediate band apply in relation to throttle opening.

1-2 ACCUMULATOR PISTON:
Stroked by 2nd oil against 1-2 accumulator oil pressure and 1-2 cushion spring force. The piston absorbs 2nd oil pressure and permits controlled intermediate band apply time and pressure.

LINE BOOST VALVE:
Prevents low or minimum line pressure operation. It is normally held open by the throttle lever and bracket assembly when T.V. cable is adjusted properly. The line boost valve will close T.V. exhaust port and boost line pressure when T.V. cable is unhooked or broken.

LO BLOW OFF VALVE:
Exhausts lo 1st oil down to 241 kPa (35 psi) to allow smooth apply of lo and reverse clutch during coast downshift.

MANUAL VALVE:
Mechanically connected to shift selector. It is fed by line oil from the pump and initiates the oil required in the various selected ranges by opening and closing ports to the RNDI, RND, lo, intermediate, and reverse passages.

PRESSURE REGULATOR VALVE:
Regulates pump output (pressure) or line pressure, converter feed lines and decrease line. It is fed by the pump and controlled by the pressure regulator spring, the T.V. boost valve, and the reverse boost valve.

PRESSURE RELIEF VALVE:
Prevents line pressure from going above 3,102 kPa (450 psi) by exhausting oil.

REVERSE BOOST VALVE:
Acted on by intermediate and reverse oil, this valve moves against the pressure regulator spring, increasing line pressure.

THROTTLE VALVE:
Regulates RNDI oil to T.V. oil pressure. Valve is controlled by T.V. plunger movement, and T.V. spring force.

T.V. BOOST VALVE:
Acted on by shift T.V. oil, this valve moves against the reverse boost valve and the pressure regulator spring force increasing line pressure.

T.V. PLUNGER:
Controlled by throttle lever and bracket assembly and linked to carburetor, this valve moves against the T.V. spring and throttle valve increasing T.V. pressure. It also controls the opening of the P.T. and detent ports.

SHIFT T.V. VALVE:
Limits T.V. oil pressure to 620 kPa (90 psi).

1-2 VALVE TRAIN:
Consists of 1-2 shift valve and 1-2 throttle valve and controls 1-2 and 2-1 shifts. 1-2 shift valve blocks drive oil when closed and allows drive oil into 2nd oil passages when open. 1-2 T.V. valve delays upshifts and downshifts according to shift T.V. pressure.

2-3 VALVE TRAIN:
Consists of 2-3 shift valve and 2-3 throttle valve and controls 2-3 and 3-2 shifts. 2-3 shift valve blocks RND oil when closed and allows RND oil into direct clutch oil passages when open. 2-3 T.V. valve delays upshifts and downshifts according to shift T.V. pressure.

3-2 CONTROL VALVE:
Regulated by governor oil, it controls the rate at which the direct clutch releases and intermediate band applies.

CHECK BALLS —

#1 — Direct clutch exhaust check ball:
Forces exhausting direct clutch oil through two orifices, resulting in an accumulated release of direct clutch and apply of intermediate band.

#2 — Direct clutch accumulator check ball:
Forces exhausting direct clutch accumulator oil to pass through an additional orifice for further accumulation.

#3 — Lo 1st Check Ball:
Forces lo 1st oil to pass through an orifice to apply the lo and reverse clutch.

#4 — Lo and Reverse Check Ball:
Separates lo and reverse oil passages to lo and reverse clutch.

#5 — Direct Clutch and Reverse Check Ball:
Separates direct clutch and reverse oil passages to direct clutch.

#6 — RNDI and Detent Check Ball:
Prevents transmission from shifting to first when above lo lockout point.

PARK

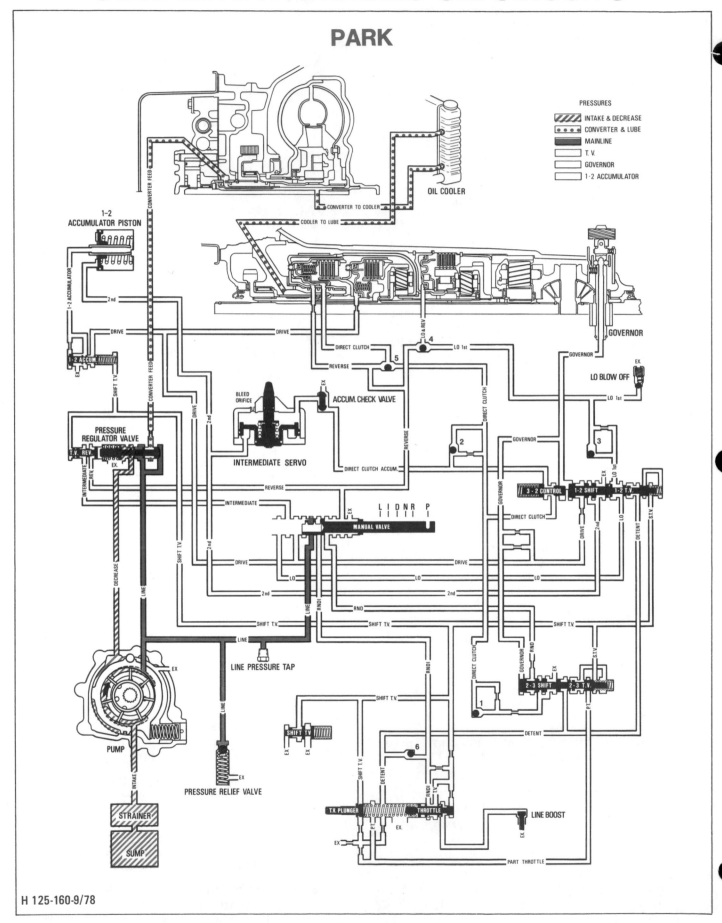

H 125-160-9/78

Figure 59 - Park—Engine Running

52

PARK-ENGINE RUNNING

DIRECT CLUTCH—RELEASED   FORWARD CLUTCH—RELEASED   LO AND REVERSE CLUTCH—RELEASED

INTERMEDIATE BAND—RELEASED   ROLLER CLUTCH—NOT HOLDING

With the selector lever in Park (P) position, oil from the pump is directed to the following:

1. Pressure Regulator Valve

2. Converter and Lubrication System

3. Pump Slide

4. Manual Valve

5. Pressure Relief Valve

6. Line Pressure Tap

Oil flows from the pump to the pressure regulator valve which regulates the pump pressure. When the pump output exceeds the demand of line pressure, oil from the pressure regulator valve is directed to the converter feed passage to fill the converter. Converter return oil is directed to the transmission cooler. Oil from the cooler is directed to the transmission lubrication system.

Oil is also directed from the pressure regulator valve to the pump slide to decrease pump output to the pressure of the regulator valve spring force, or 482 kPa (70 psi). Line pressure acts on the pressure relief valve which will exhaust any oil above 2068 to 3102 kPa (300 - 450 psi).

Line pressure at the manual valve is available for use in other drive ranges.

SUMMARY

The converter is filled; all clutches and the band are released. Manual linkage has the parking pawl engaged in the reaction internal gear lugs. The transmission is in Park (P). Line pressure is regulated to approximately 483 kPa (70 psi).

NEUTRAL-ENGINE RUNNING

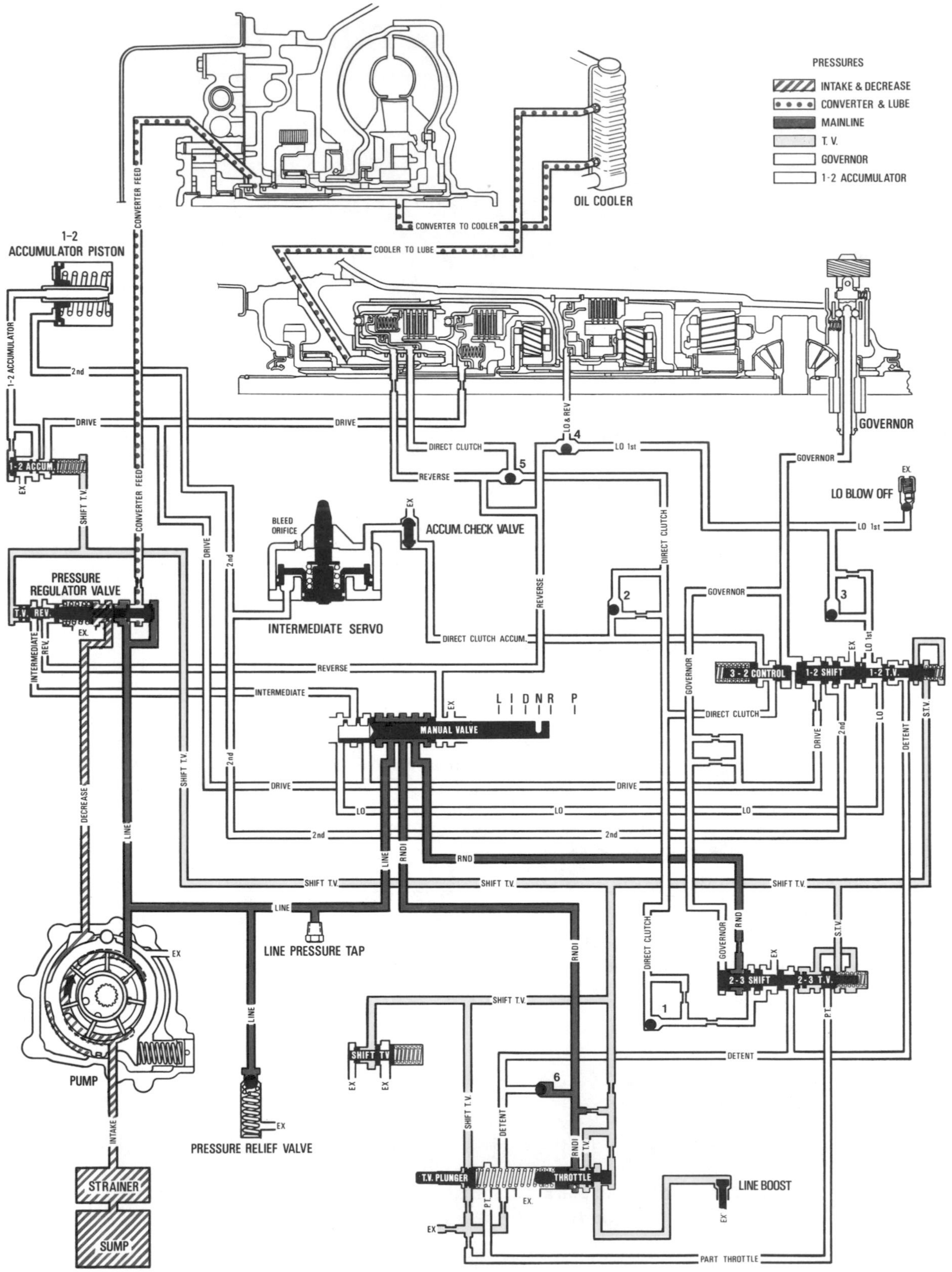

H 125-161-9/78

Figure 60 - Neutral—Engine Running

NEUTRAL-ENGINE RUNNING

DIRECT CLUTCH—RELEASED **FORWARD CLUTCH—RELEASED** **LO AND REVERSE CLUTCH—RELEASED**

INTERMEDIATE BAND—RELEASED **ROLLER CLUTCH—NOT HOLDING**

When the selector lever is moved to the Neutral (N) position, the manual valve is positioned to allow line pressure to enter two (2) passages as follows:

FIRST—It enters the reverse, neutral, drive, intermediate (RNDI) passage. RNDI oil is directed to the seat RNDI and detent check ball (6), and to the throttle valve where it is regulated to a variable pressure called throttle valve (T.V.) pressure. T.V. pressure increases with carburetor opening and is directed to the shift throttle valve. This valve limits shift T.V. oil pressure from going above 620 kPa (90 psi).

Shift T.V. oil is then directed to the 1-2 and 2-3 throttle valves, T.V. boost valve, T.V. plunger and the 1-2 accumulator valve.

Shift T.V. oil acting on the T.V. boost valve will boost line pressure according to throttle opening.

SECOND—Line pressure enters the reverse, neutral, drive (RND) passage and is directed to a land on the 2-3 shift valve.

SUMMARY

The converter is filled; all the clutches and the band are released; the transmission is in Neutral (N).

DRIVE RANGE-FIRST GEAR

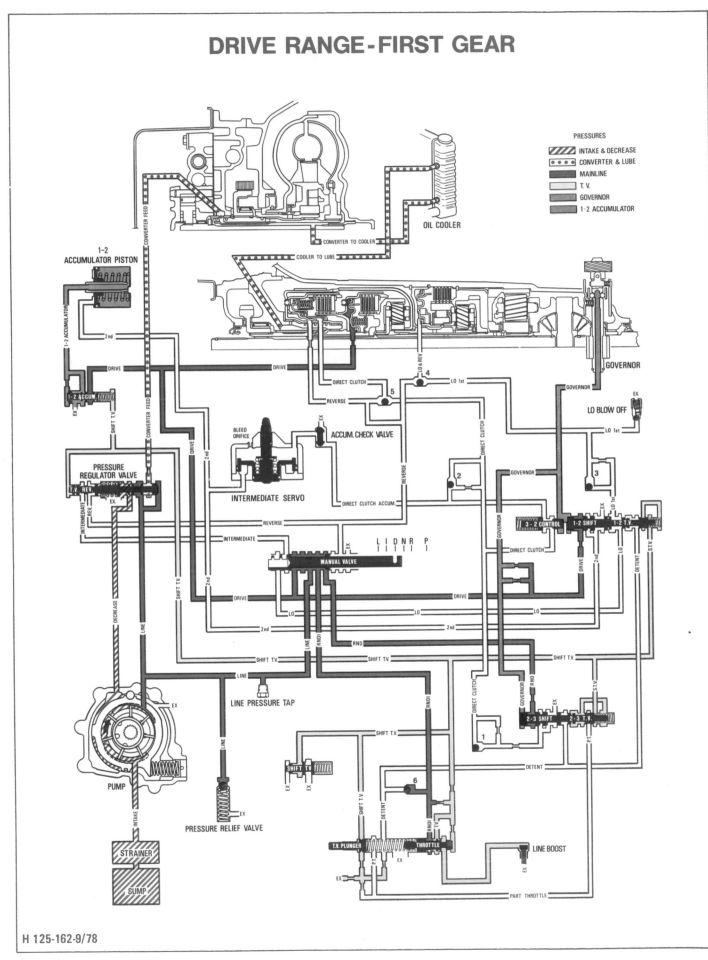

Figure 61 - Drive Range—First Gear

DRIVE RANGE - FIRST GEAR

FORWARD CLUTCH—APPLIED   ROLLER CLUTCH—HOLDING

When the selector lever is moved to Drive (D) position, the manual valve is repositioned to allow line pressure to enter the drive passage. Drive oil then flows to the following:

1. Forward Clutch

2. Governor Assembly

3. 1-2 Shift Valve

4. 1-2 Accumulator Valve

BASIC CONTROL

Drive oil is directed to the forward clutch through an orifice where it acts on the clutch piston to apply the forward clutch.

Drive oil is directed to the 1-2 shift valve.

Drive oil is directed to the 1-2 accumulator valve and is regulated to a pressure called 1-2 accumulator pressure; this pressure is directed to the 1-2 accumulator piston to act as a cushion for the band apply on a 1-2 shift.

Drive oil at the governor assembly is regulated to another variable pressure called governor pressure. Governor pressure increases with vehicle speed and acts against the 1-2 and 2-3 shift valves and the 3-2 control valve.

SUMMARY

The converter is filled; the forward clutch is applied; the transmission is in Drive (D) range — first gear.

DRIVE RANGE-SECOND GEAR

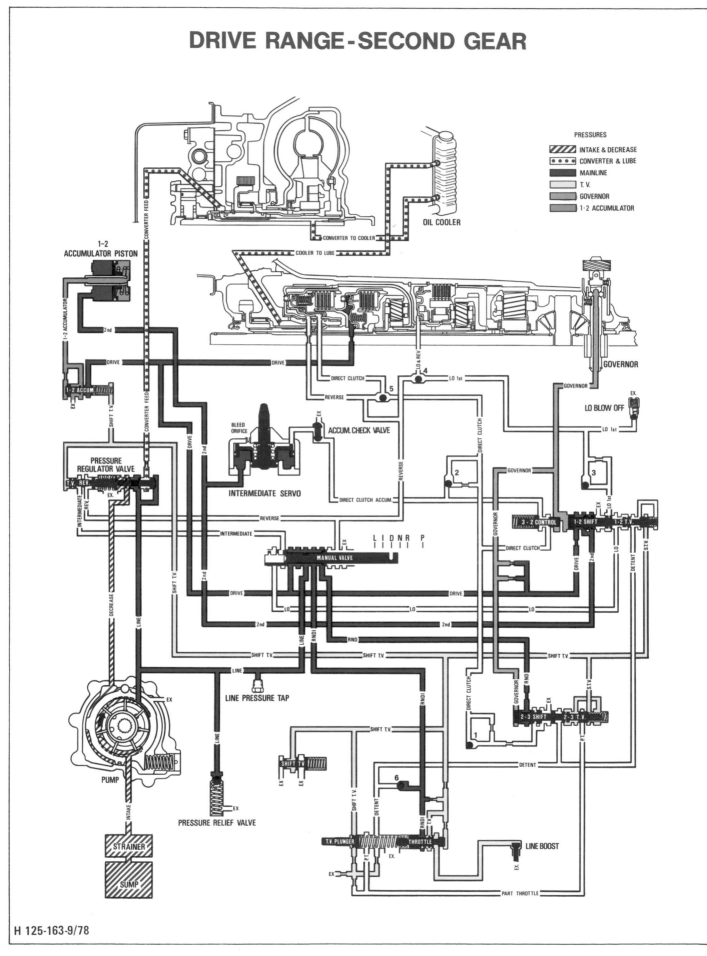

Figure 62 - Drive Range—Second Gear

DRIVE RANGE-SECOND GEAR

FORWARD CLUTCH—APPLIED   INTERMEDIATE BAND—APPLIED

As both vehicle speed and governor pressure increase, the force of governor oil acting on the 1-2 shift valve overcomes the pressure of shift T.V. oil and the force of the 1-2 T.V. spring. This allows the 1-2 valve to open and drive oil to enter the second (2nd) oil passage. This oil is called second (2nd) oil.

Second oil from the 1-2 shift valve is directed to the following:

1. Intermediate servo
2. 1-2 Accumulator piston

BASIC CONTROL

Second oil from the 1-2 shift valve is directed to the intermediate servo to apply the intermediate band. At the same time, 2nd oil moves the 1-2 accumulator piston against 1-2 accumulator pressure and the accumulator spring to maintain a controlled build up of pressure on the intermediate servo during the 1-2 shift for a smooth band apply.

SUMMARY

The forward clutch and intermediate band are applied; the transmission is in Drive (D) range — second gear.

DRIVE RANGE-THIRD GEAR

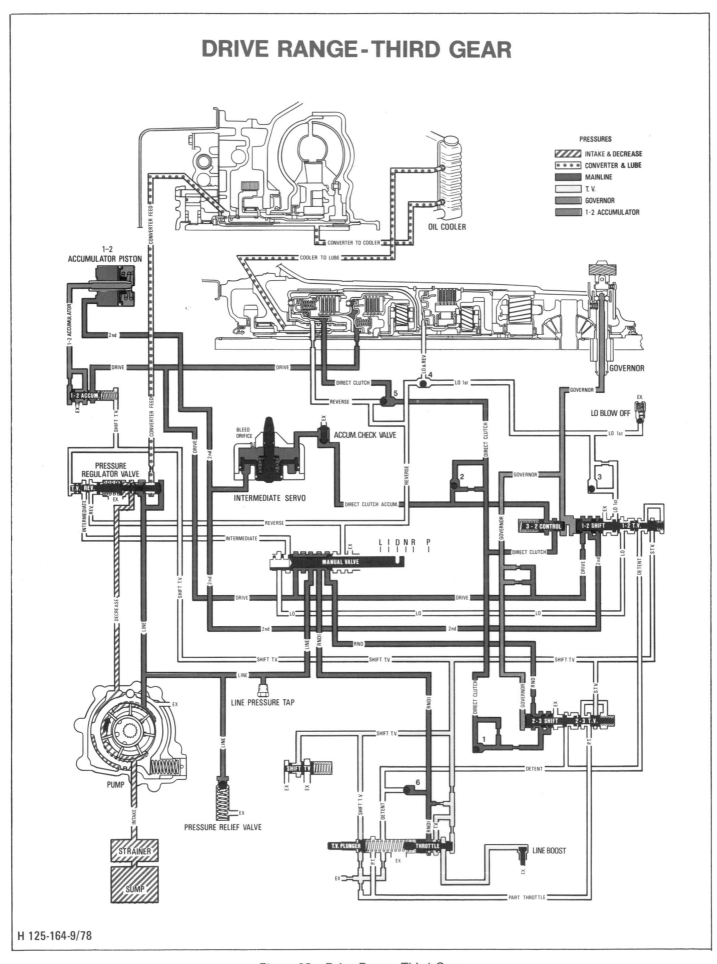

Figure 63 - Drive Range—Third Gear

DRIVE RANGE - THIRD GEAR

FORWARD CLUTCH—APPLIED   DIRECT CLUTCH—APPLIED

As both vehicle speed and governor pressure increase, the force of governor oil acting on the 2-3 shift valve overcomes the force of the 2-3 T.V. spring and shift T.V. oil. This allows the 2-3 shift valve to open and RND oil enters the direct clutch oil passage. This oil is called direct clutch oil.

Direct clutch oil from the 2-3 shift valve is directed to the following:

1. Direct clutch exhaust check ball (1)

2. 3-2 control valve

3. Direct clutch and reverse check ball (5)

4. Direct clutch accumulator check ball (2)

5. Accumulator check valve

6. Intermediate servo

BASIC CONTROL

Direct clutch oil from the 2-3 shift valve flows past the direct clutch exhaust check ball (1), to the direct clutch and reverse check ball (5), seating it in the reverse passage, and to the inner area of the direct clutch piston, applying the direct clutch. At the same time, direct clutch oil is directed past the direct clutch accumulator check ball (2) into the direct clutch accumulator passage, where it is called direct clutch accumulator oil, to the direct clutch accumulator check valve, seating it; and to the release side of the intermediate servo. The pressure of the direct clutch accumulator oil combined with the servo cushion spring, moves the servo piston against 2nd oil and acts as an accumulator for a smooth intermediate band release and direct clutch apply.

Direct clutch oil also flows through the 3-2 control valve to the direct clutch accumulator passage.

SUMMARY

The forward and direct clutches are applied and the intermediate band is released; the transmission is in Drive (D) range — third gear (direct drive).

PART THROTTLE 3-2 DOWNSHIFT

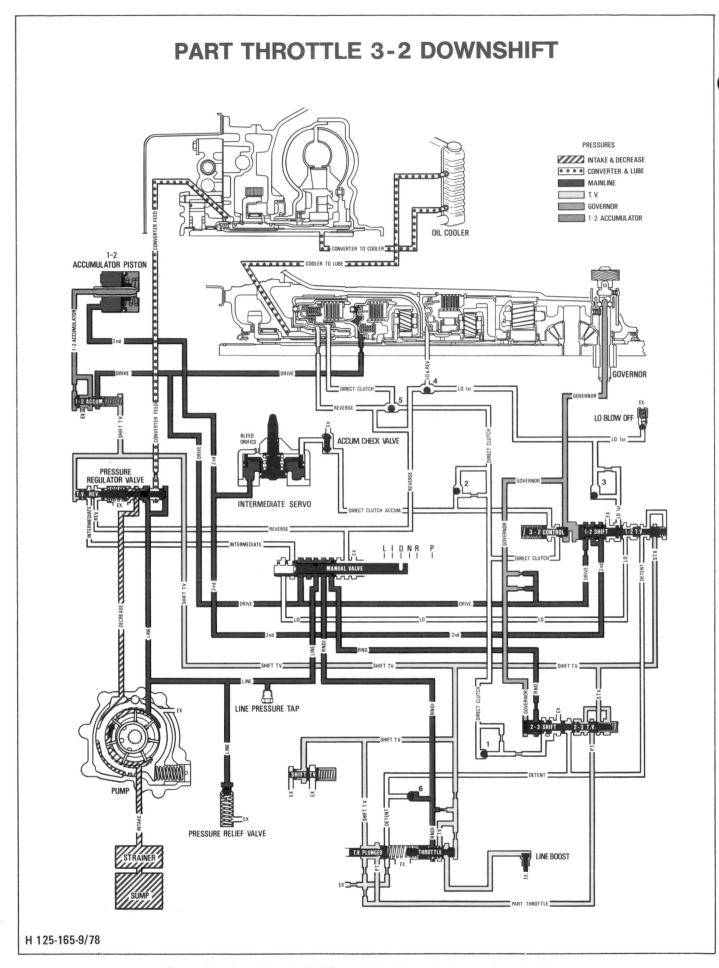

Figure 64 - Part Throttle 3-2 Downshift—Valves in Second Gear Position

H 125-165-9/78

62

PART THROTTLE 3-2 DOWNSHIFT

Valves In Second Gear Position

FORWARD CLUTCH—APPLIED   INTERMEDIATE BAND—APPLIED

A part throttle 3-2 downshift can be accomplished below approximately 50 mph (80 km/h) by depressing the accelerator pedal far enough to move the throttle valve (T.V.) plunger to allow shift T.V. oil to enter the part throttle (P.T.) passage. This oil, called part throttle (P.T.) oil, is then routed to the 2-3 T.V. valve.

Part throttle oil and the 2-3 spring force will close the 2-3 shift valve against governor oil, shutting off RND oil to the direct clutch passage. Exhausting direct clutch oil seats the direct clutch exhaust check ball (1), flows through the two orifices, and is exhausted at the 2-3 shift valve. At the same time, direct clutch accumulator oil from the intermediate servo also exhausts through the same route as directed clutch oil. Second oil acting on the servo piston applies the band for a smooth band apply as the direct clutch is released.

DETENT DOWNSHIFT

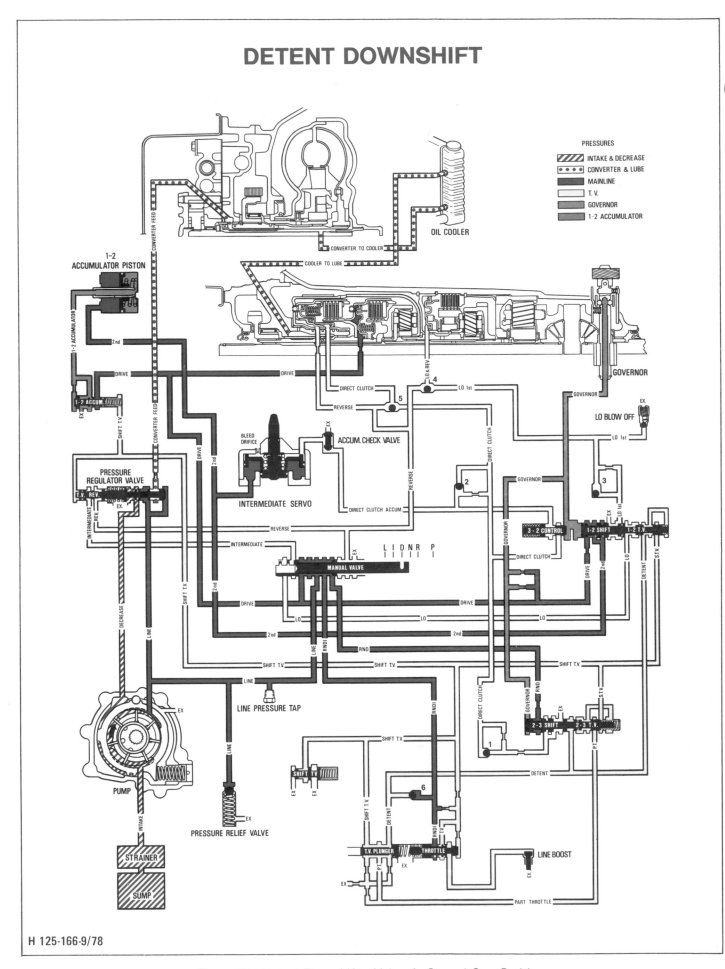

Figure 65 - Detent Downshifts—Valves in Second Gear Position

DETENT DOWNSHIFTS

Valves In Second Gear Position

FORWARD CLUTCH—APPLIED   INTERMEDIATE BAND—APPLIED

While operating at speeds below approximately 65 mph (105 km/h), a forced or detent 3-2 downshift is possible by depressing the accelerator pedal fully. This will position the throttle valve (T.V.) plunger to allow shift T.V. oil to enter the detent passage. This oil, called detent oil, is then routed to the following:

1. 2-3 throttle valve

2. 1-2 throttle valve

3. RNDI and detent check ball (6)

Detent oil from the T.V. plunger flows to the 2-3 throttle valve. Detent and part throttle (P.T.) oil pressure combined with the 2-3 spring force will close the 2-3 shift valve against governor oil and allow direct clutch oil through two orifices to exhaust at the 2-3 shift valve.

At high vehicle speeds, above approximately 50 mph (80 km/h), governor oil acting on the 3-2 control valve will close it. Now the exhausting direct clutch accumulator oil from the intermediate servo will seat the direct clutch accumulator check ball (2) and flow through another orifice controlling the intermediate band apply for a smooth 3-2 shift at high speeds.

A detent 2-1 downshift can be accomplished at speeds below approximately 30 mph (48 km/h), because detent oil pressure and the 1-2 spring force acting on the 1-2 throttle valve will close the 1-2 shift valve, shifting the transmission to first gear.

Detent oil acts on the RNDI and detent check ball (6) but will not unseat it because RNDI oil is at a higher pressure.

INTERMEDIATE RANGE

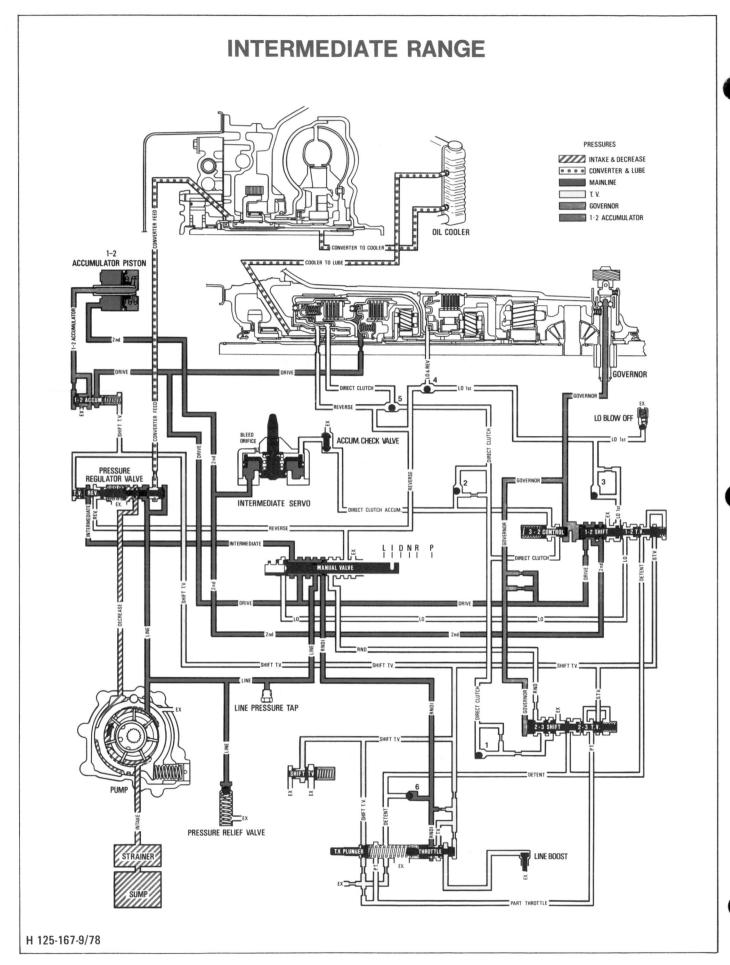

Figure 66 - Intermediate Range

H 125-167-9/78

INTERMEDIATE RANGE

INTERMEDIATE BAND– APPLIED   FORWARD CLUTCH–APPLIED

A 3-2 downshift can be accomplished by moving the selector lever from Drive (D) range to Intermediate range.

When the selector lever is in Intermediate position, RND oil will exhaust at the manual valve. Intermediate oil from the manual valve is directed between the reverse and T.V. boost valves.

Intermediate oil acting on the reverse boost valve plus the pressure regulator spring force will boost line pressure to 827 kPa (120 psi) which is required to hold the intermediate band and forward clutch on.

Because RND oil is exhausted, the transmission will shift to 2nd gear, regardless of vehicle speed. (RND oil is the feed for direct clutch oil in 3rd gear.) With the transmission in 2nd gear, Intermediate range, it cannot upshift to 3rd gear regardless of vehicle speed.

SUMMARY

The forward clutch and intermediate band are applied. The transmission is in Intermediate range-second gear.

LO RANGE

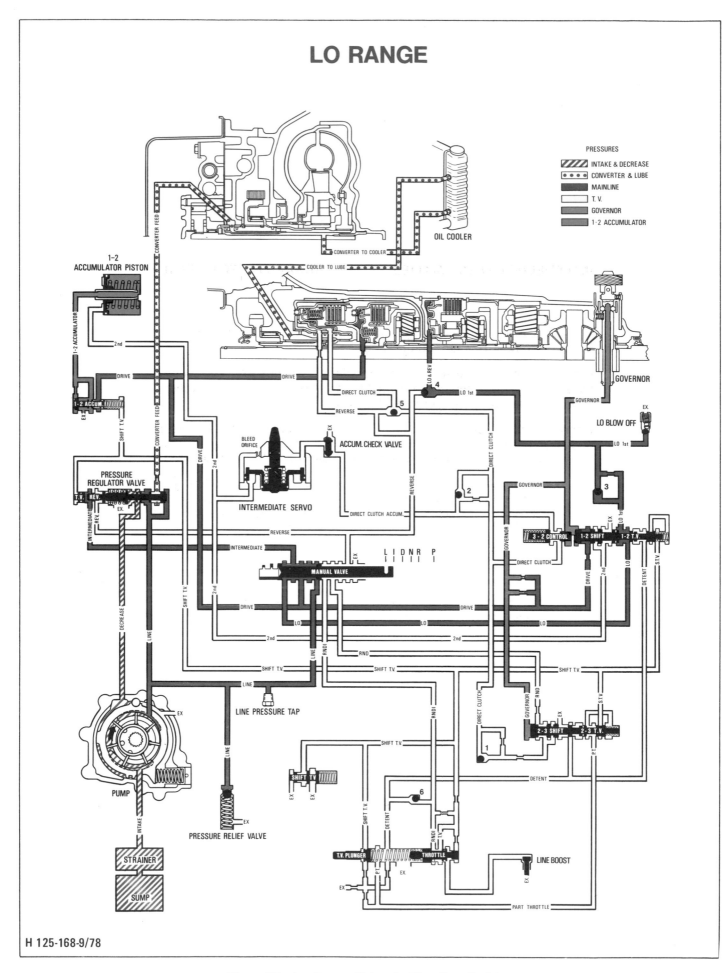

Figure 67 - Lo Range—Valves in First Gear Position

H 125-168-9/78

LO RANGE

Valves In First Gear Position

FORWARD CLUTCH—APPLIED   **LO AND REVERSE CLUTCH—APPLIED**

Maximum downhill braking can be attained at speeds below approximately 40 mph (64 km/h) with the selector lever in Lo range position. Lo range oil pressure is the same as intermediate 827 kPa (120 psi) because intermediate oil is still present.

Lo oil from the manual valve is directed to the 1-2 throttle valve. Lo oil pressure and the 1-2 T.V. spring force will close the 1-2 shift valve at speeds below approximately 40 mph (64 km/h). This allows lo oil to enter the lo 1st passage where it seats the lo 1st check ball (3) and passes through an orifice to the lo blow off valve, which exhausts lo 1st oil down to 241 kPa (35 psi). The lo 1st oil is then directed to seat the lo and reverse check ball (4) and to the lo and reverse clutch for a smooth apply.

SUMMARY

The forward clutch is applied. The lo and reverse clutch is applied. The transmission is in Lo range — first gear.

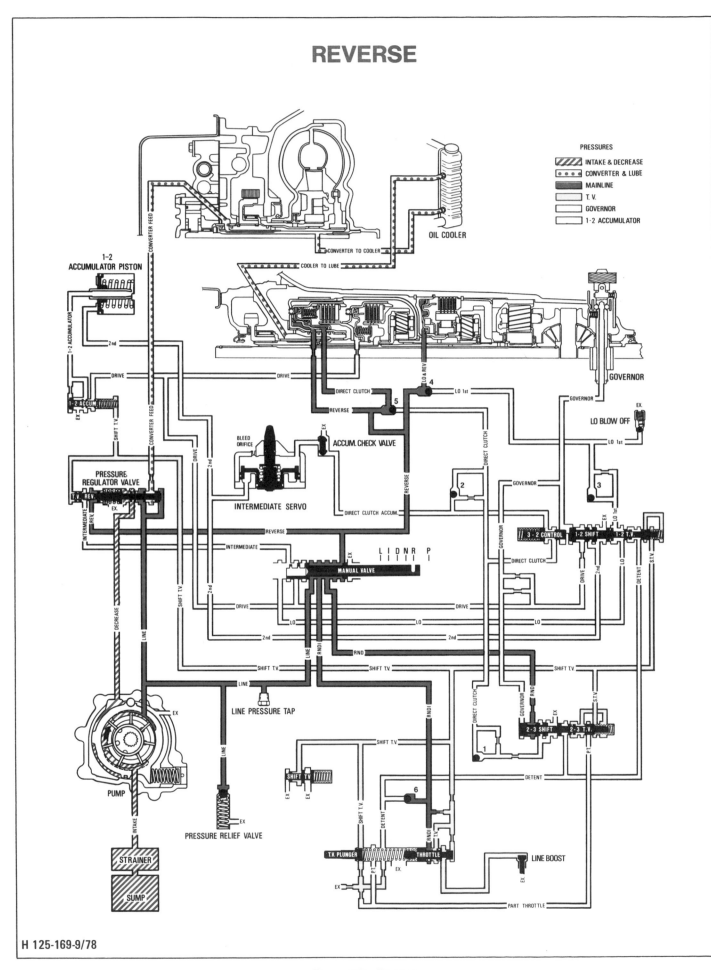

Figure 68 - Reverse

REVERSE

When the selector lever is moved to the Reverse (R) position, the manual valve is repositioned to allow line pressure to enter three (3) passages, as follows:

1.   Reverse

2.   RNDI (Reverse, Neutral, Drive and Intermediate)

3.   RND (Reverse, Neutral, and Drive)

FIRST—Reverse oil from the manual valve seats direct clutch and reverse check ball (5) in the direct clutch passage and flows to both the inner and outer areas of the clutch piston, applying the direct clutch. Reverse oil also seats the lo and reverse check ball (4) in the lo 1st passage and applies the lo and reverse clutch. Reverse oil flows to the reverse boost valve and will boost reverse line pressure to about 827 kPa (120 psi).

SECOND—RNDI oil from the manual valve flows to the throttle valve and is regulated to T.V. pressure. T.V. oil flows through the shift T.V. valve and is limited by it to approximately 620 kPa (90 psi).

Oil from the shift T.V. valve is directed to the T.V. boost valve. Shift T.V. oil acting on the T.V. boost valve will boost reverse line pressure to approximately 1447 kPa (210 psi).

THIRD—RND oil from the manual valve is directed to the 2-3 shift valve, but this has no function in Reverse.

SUMMARY

The direct clutch is applied. The lo and reverse clutch is applied. The transmission is in Reverse (R).

NOTES

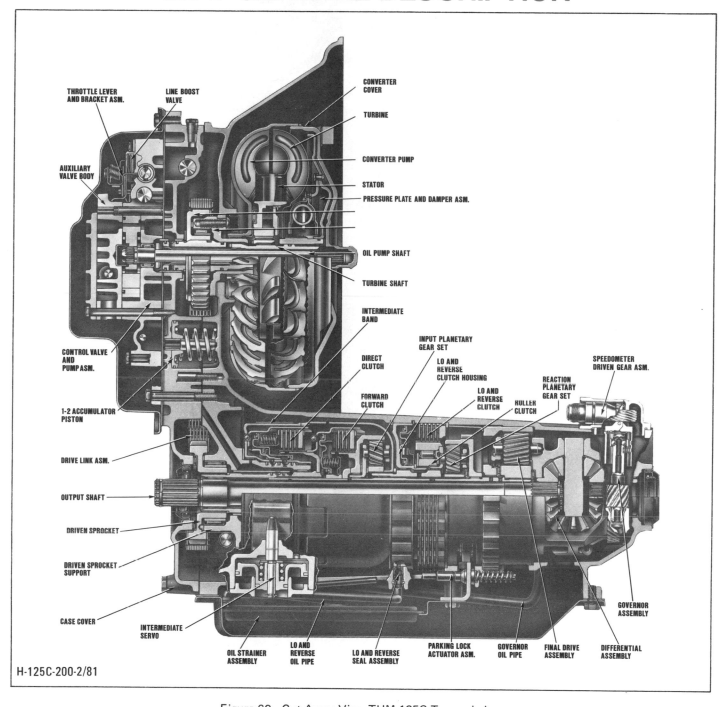

Figure 69 - Cut-Away View THM 125C Transmission

GENERAL DESCRIPTION

The THM 125C automatic transaxle is a fully automatic unit consisting primarily of a 4-element hydraulic torque converter, compound planetary gear set and dual sprocket and drive link assembly. In addition, this transaxle incorporates a differential and final drive gear set.

The 4-element torque converter contains a pump, a turbine, a pressure plate splined to the turbine, and a stator assembly. The pressure plate, when applied, provides a mechanical direct drive coupling of the engine to the planetary gear.

Three multiple-disc clutches, a roller clutch and a band provide the friction elements required to obtain the desired function of the planetary gear sets.

A hydraulic system pressurized by a vane type pump provides the working pressure required to operate the friction elements and automatic controls.

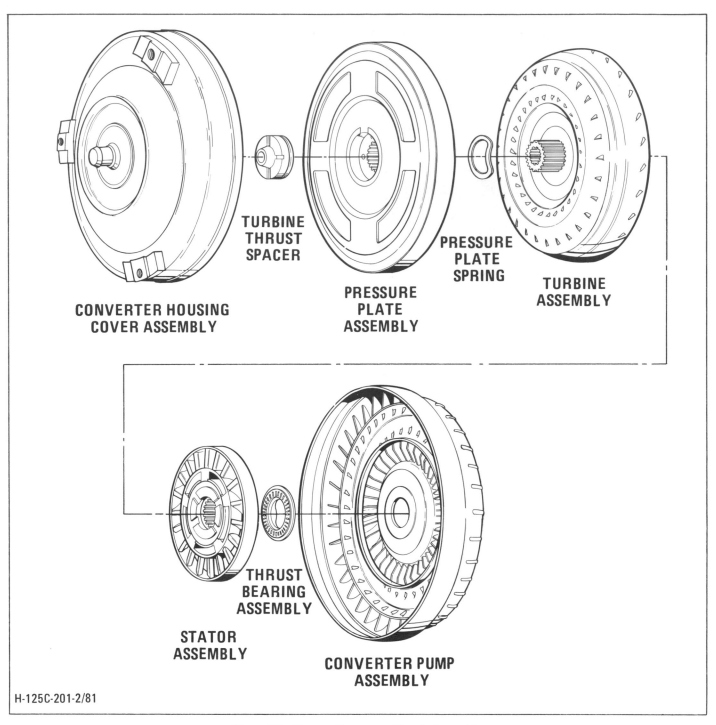

TURBINE THRUST SPACER

PRESSURE PLATE SPRING

CONVERTER HOUSING COVER ASSEMBLY

PRESSURE PLATE ASSEMBLY

TURBINE ASSEMBLY

THRUST BEARING ASSEMBLY

STATOR ASSEMBLY

CONVERTER PUMP ASSEMBLY

H-125C-201-2/81

Figure 70 - Torque Converter Clutch Assembly

CONVERTER CLUTCH OPERATION

The apply or release of the converter clutch is determined by the direction the feed oil is routed to the converter. When oil is fed between the cover and the clutch plate, the converter is released. When oil is fed on the turbine side of the clutch plate, the clutch is applied.

To aid in reducing torsional shock during converter clutch apply, a damper assembly is incorporated in the converter clutch pressure plate. The spring loaded damper assembly is splined to the converter turbine assembly. The converter clutch pressure plate is attached to the pivoting mechanism of

the damper assembly. This pivoting action allows the pressure plate to rotate independent of the damper assembly, up to approximately 45°. The rate of independent rotation is controlled by the pivoting mechanism acting on the springs in the damper assembly. The spring cushioning effect of the damper assembly aids in reducing converter clutch apply "feel".

To further aid the apply and release of the converter clutch during various driving situations, controls have been incorporated in the electrical system.

74

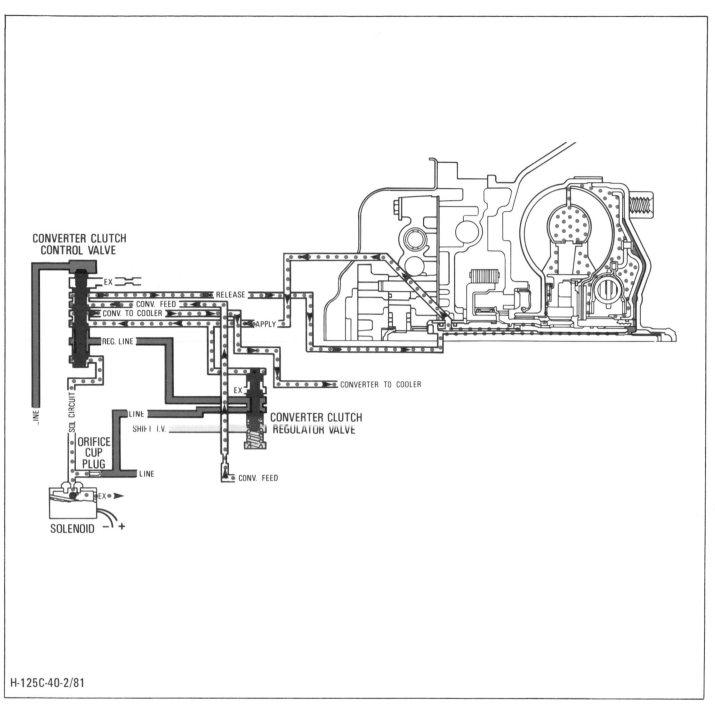

CONVERTER CLUTCH
CONTROL VALVE

EX

CONV. FEED

CONV. TO COOLER

RELEASE

APPLY

REG. LINE

CONVERTER TO COOLER

EX

LINE

SOL CIRCUIT

SHIFT I.V.

CONVERTER CLUTCH
REGULATOR VALVE

ORIFICE
CUP
PLUG

LINE

LINE

CONV. FEED

EX

SOLENOID − +

H-125C-40-2/81

Figure 71 - T.C.C. Release

The apply or release of the converter clutch is determined by the direction that the converter feed oil is routed to the converter. The converter feed oil from the pressure regulator valve flows to the converter clutch control valve. The position of the converter clutch control valve controls which direction converter feed oil flows to the converter.

The converter clutch control valve is held in the release position in park, neutral, reverse, drive range 1st gear and 2nd gear, by line pressure acting on the end of the converter clutch apply valve. With the converter clutch control valve in the release position, converter feed oil flows into the converter

clutch release passages. It then flows between the pump drive shaft and turbine shaft to the front or release side of the converter clutch, between the converter clutch pressure plate and the converter cover. This moves the converter clutch pressure plate away from the converter cover, releasing the converter clutch and charging the converter with oil. The oil then leaves the converter by flowing through the turbine shaft into the converter clutch apply oil circuit. The apply oil circuit is now being used in a reverse direction. The oil then flows from the apply passage into the cooler passage and to the lubrication system.

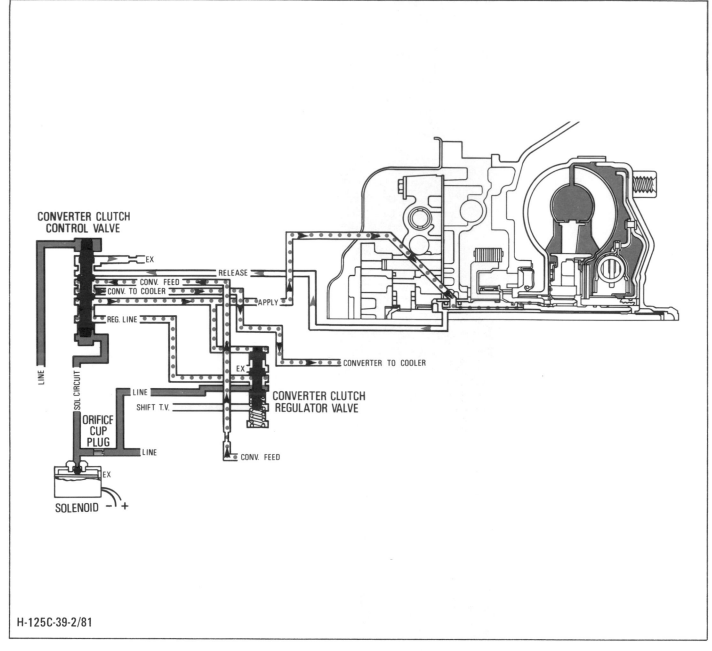

Figure 72 - T.C.C. Apply

To prevent the converter clutch from applying in drive range 3rd gear, at car speeds below converter clutch engagement speeds, the C3 or governor pressure switch (depending on system) will break the circuit to the solenoid exhaust valve. This de-energizes the solenoid and opens the exhaust valve to exhaust the solenoid circuit oil at the converter clutch control valve. Line pressure then holds the converter clutch control valve in the release position.

When car speed in drive range 3rd gear, reaches converter clutch engagement speed, the C3 or governor pressure switch (depending on system) will activate the solenoid, closing the exhaust valve. This allows solenoid circuit oil to move the converter clutch control valve against line pressure. With the converter clutch control valve in the apply position, regulated line oil, from the converter clutch regulator valve, is allowed to pass into the converter apply passage. It then flows through the turbine shaft to the apply side of the converter clutch. The regulated line oil, from the converter clutch regulator valve, controls the apply feel of the pressure plate.

As the pressure plate begins to move to its applied position, release oil on the front side of the pressure plate is redirected back between the turbine shaft and pump drive shaft and exhausted at the converter clutch control valve through an orifice, to time the clutch apply. When the converter clutch control valve moved to the apply position, orificed converter feed oil entered the converter to cooler passage to provide oil to the lubrication system.

Converter Clutch Applied

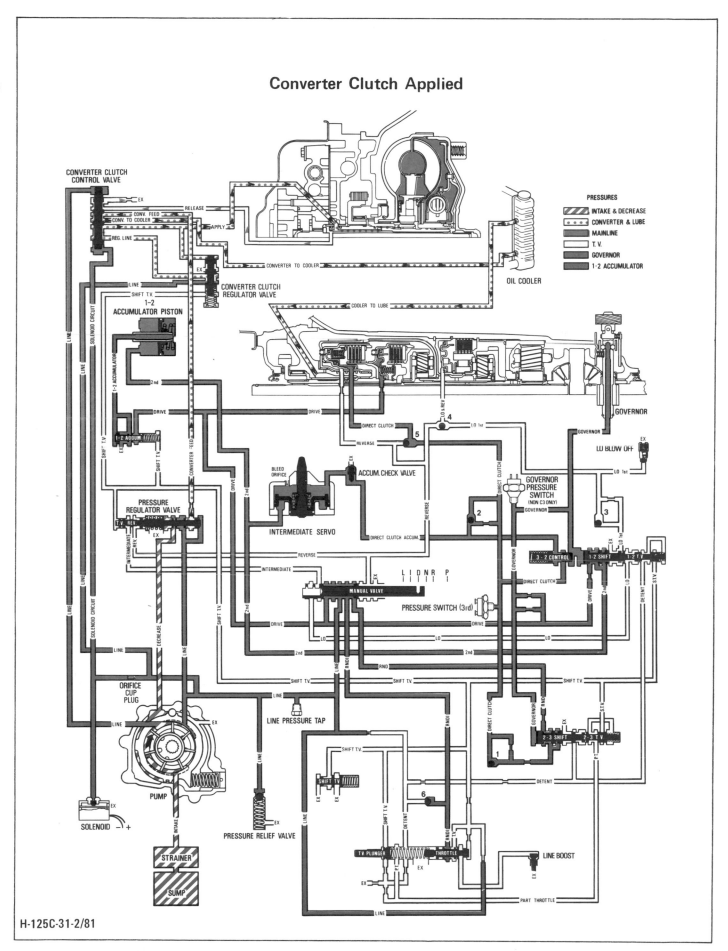

Figure 73 - Oil Circuit—Converter Clutch Applied

H-125C-31-2/81

Converter Clutch Released

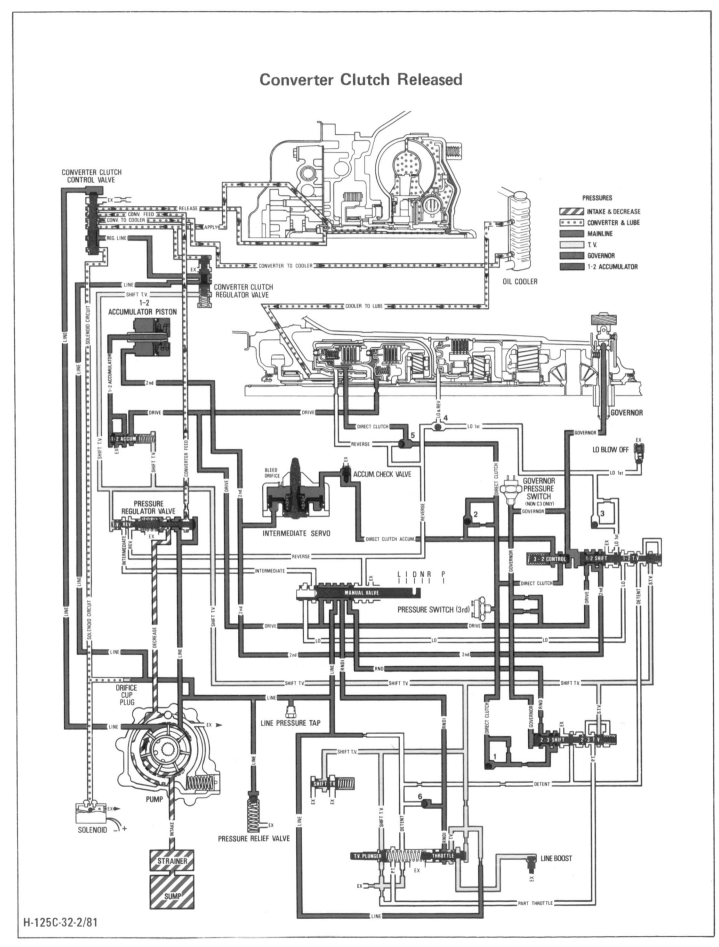

H-125C-32-2/81

Figure 74 - Oil Circuit—Converter Clutch Released

TORQUE CONVERTER CLUTCH ELECTRICAL CONTROLS

Two different electrical systems are used to control the apply of the torque converter clutch. Both systems use a solenoid and 3rd clutch pressure switch, but the vehicle speed sensing controls are not the same.

1. Cars equipped with computer command control (C3) use this system to energize the solenoid when a certain speed has been reached.

2. Cars **not** equipped with computer command control (C3) use a governor pressure switch to energize the solenoid when a certain speed has been reached.

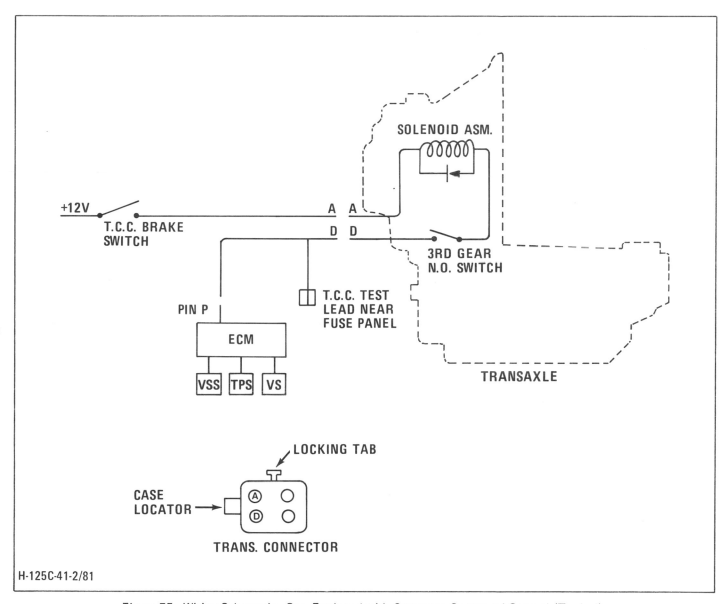

H-125C-41-2/81

Figure 75 - Wiring Schematic—Cars Equipped with Computer Command Control (Typical)

CARS EQUIPPED WITH COMPUTER COMMAND CONTROL

1. Brake Release Switch — To avoid stalling the engine when braking, any time the brakes are applied the converter clutch is released.

2. Electronic Control Module — Energizes and grounds transmission electrical system.

3. Vehicle Speed Sensor — Sends vehicle speed information to the electronic control module.

4. Throttle Position Sensor — Sends throttle position information to electronic control module.

5. Vacuum Sensor — Sends engine vacuum (load) information to electronic control module.

79

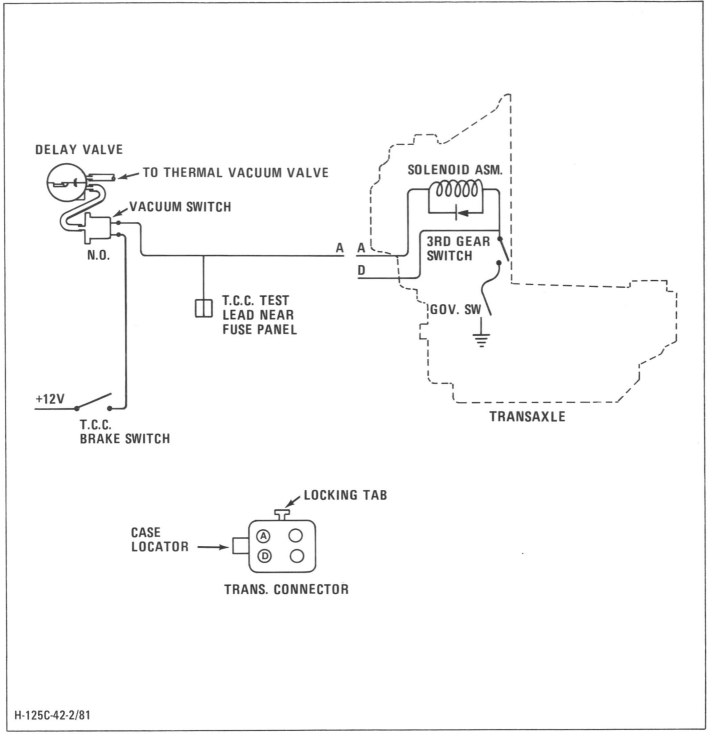

Figure 76 - Wiring Schematic—Cars Not Equipped with Computer Command Control (Typical)

CARS NOT EQUIPPED WITH COMPUTER COMMAND CONTROL

1. Brake Release Switch — To avoid stalling the engine when braking, any time the brakes are applied the converter clutch is released.

2. Thermal Vacuum Valve — Prevents the converter clutch from applying until the engine coolant temperature has reached 130° F.

3. Engine Vacuum Switch — Releases the converter clutch when engine vacuum drops to approxi-

mately 1.5 - 3 inches during moderate acceleration, prior to a part-throttle or detent downshift.

4. Vacuum Delay Valve — Slows the vacuum switch response to vacuum changes.

5. Ported Vacuum — Source of vacuum to vacuum switch; opens the vacuum switch to release the clutch during a closed throttle coast down.

125/125C
SYSTEMATIC TROUBLESHOOTING

INDEX

The key to correcting a complaint is to make use of all of the available symptoms and logically letting them direct you to the cause. Symptoms or conditions that will help are determined by subjective road tests, oil pressure checks or noise evaluation.

When dealing with automatic transmission complaints, it is best to gather as many symptoms as possible before making the decision to remove the transmission from the vehicle. Remember, the vehicle is the best test stand and diagnostic tool available to you, if the transmission is operable. Once the trans-

mission is on the bench, it cannot tell you "What Hurts", and quite frequently the correction of the cause of the complaint does not require removal of the transmission from the vehicle.

Select from the index the condition that best represents the problem and the proper page or chart will direct you to perform specific checks. Then, road test the vehicle. The charts were planned to help you find the cause of the problem in the most logical sequence.

CHECKING TRANSMISSION OIL LEVEL

NOTICE: Due to the shape of the filler tube, oil level readings may be misleading. Look carefully for full oil ring on both sides of dipstick. Recheck if any question of oil level occurs.

1.   Place transmission in "Park" and leave in "Park".   DO NOT MOVE LEVER THROUGH RANGES.

2.   Brakes applied.

3.   Vehicle on level surface.

4.   Start engine.

5.   Check oil level on dipstick.

6.   If oil is low, check for possible causes, pages 97 and 98.

NOTICE: "COLD" reading is above "FULL" mark.

With the oil temperature cold and the selector left in the Park position (DO NOT SHIFT LEVER THROUGH RANGES) the oil level should read:

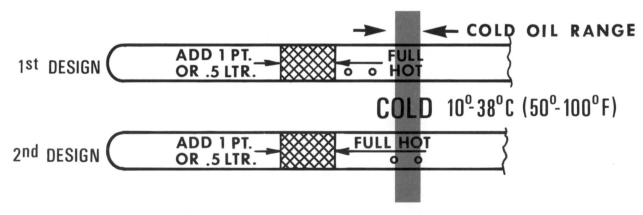

With the oil temperature hot [obtained after at least 15 miles (24 Km) of driving] and selector lever shifted through the ranges, the oil level should read:

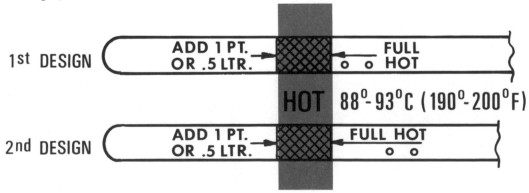

NOTICE: Maintain oil level in the "HOT" range at normal operating temperatures.

NOTICE: Do not overfill transmission, as this may cause foaming and loss of oil through the vent.

MANUAL LINKAGE ADJUSTMENT

The transmission manual linkage must be adjusted so that the indicator quadrant and stops, correspond with the transmission detents. If the linkage is not adjusted properly, an internal leak could occur which could cause a clutch or band to slip.

Refer to the car division shop manual for manual linkage adjustment procedure.

CAUTION: If a manual linkage adjustment is made, with the selector lever in the "Park" position, the parking pawl should freely engage the reaction internal gear to prevent the car from rolling. Transmission, vehicle or personal injury may occur if not properly adjusted.

T.V. CABLE SYSTEM

GENERAL DESCRIPTION

The T.V. cable used on the THM 125 controls line pressure, shift points, shift feel, part throttle downshifts and detent downshifts. The function of the cable is similar to the function of the THM 200 (M-29) transmission. The cable operates the throttle lever and bracket assembly. (See Figure 77.)

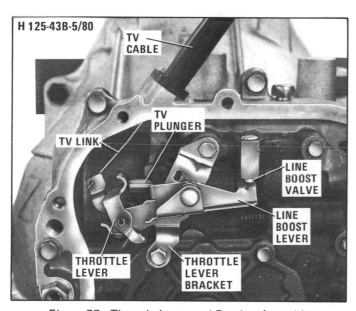

Figure 77 - Throttle Lever and Bracket Assembly

The Throttle Lever and Bracket Assembly serves two (2) basic functions:

1. The primary function of this assembly is to transfer the carburetor throttle plate movement to the T.V. plunger in the control valve pump assembly as related by the T.V. cable and linkage. This causes T.V. pressure and line pressure to increase according to throttle opening and also controls part throttle and detent downshifts. The proper adjustment of the T.V. cable is based on the T.V. plunger being fully depressed to flush with the T.V. bushing at wide open throttle.

2. The second function of the assembly involves the line boost lever and line boost valve. The function of this system is to prevent the transmission from operating at low (idle position) pressures, if the T.V. cable should become broken or disconnected. If the cable is connected, not broken or stretched, the line boost lever will not move from its normal, spring loaded, up position which holds the line boost valve off its seat. The line boost lever will drop down to allow the line boost valve to seat only if the cable is broken, disconnected or extremely out of adjustment (see Figure 78). With the valve body cover removed, it should be possible to pull down on the line boost lever and when released, the lever spring should return the lever to normal up position. If the throttle lever and bracket assembly binds or sticks so that the line boost lever cannot lift the line boost valve off its seat, high line pressures and delayed upshifts will result.

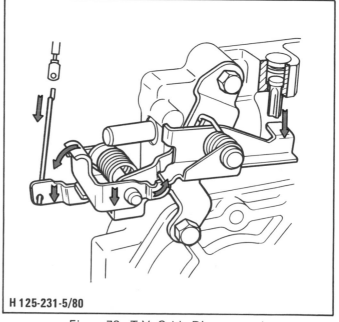

Figure 78 - T.V. Cable Disconnected

DIAGNOSIS PROCEDURE

1. Check transmission oil level and correct as required.

2. Be sure engine is operating properly and brakes are not dragging.

3. Check for correct T.V. cable, according to the parts catalog.

4. Check that the T.V. cable is connected at both ends.

5. Check the T.V. cable for sticking or binding:
   a. Engine running at idle speed.
   b. Transmission selector in Neutral with vehicle BRAKES SET.
   c. Pull the T.V. cable to full throttle position.
   d. Release the cable. The cable should return to the closed throttle position. If the T.V. cable sticks, it may be caused by one or more of the following:
      1) Sharp bends or a damaged T.V. cable housing. Correct by re-routing the cable or replace it if required.
      2) Sharp end or burr on the T.V. link, dragging in the T.V. cable housing. Correct by making end smooth, using a file or stone.
      3) Bent T.V. link. Replace as required.
      4) Damaged or binding throttle lever and bracket assembly. Correct by straightening or replace as required.

5) Throttle lever spring un-hooked or damaged.

6. If the T.V. cable is adjusted too long, it may result in one of the two following conditions:
   a. Early and slipping shifts and/or no detent downshifts.
   b. Delayed or full throttle shifts by causing the transmission to operate in the high pressure mode. The transmission senses a malfunction of the T.V. cable and associated parts; and to prevent burning the clutches and band due to low line pressures, it will go into the high pressure mode. Line pressures checked under the "minimum T.V." conditions in Neutral and Drive will be in the range of the "full T.V." pressures, if the transmission is in the high pressure mode (see Oil Pressure Chart). The complaint could be described as no up-shifts, delayed or sharp upshifts; and the closed throttle 3-2 shifts may automatically occur as high as 45 m.p.h. (72 km/h).

7. If the T.V. cable is adjusted too short, it will result in raising the line pressure and shift points. It may also limit the carburetor opening to prevent full throttle operation.

8. Readjust the T.V. cable using the procedure on page 7. The cable housing should now extend through the cable snap lock assembly about 1.57 - 7.95 mm (1/16" - 5/16"). (See Figure 79.)

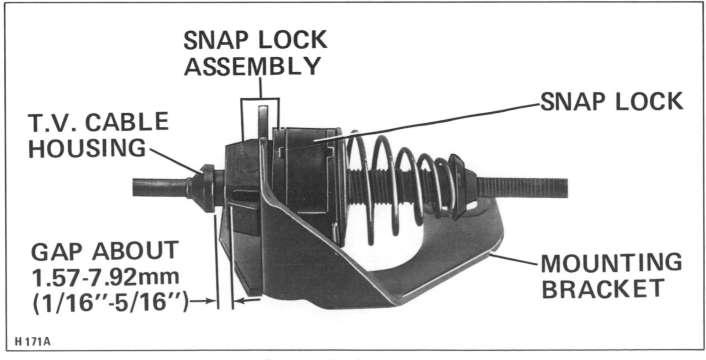

SNAP LOCK ASSEMBLY

SNAP LOCK

T.V. CABLE HOUSING

GAP ABOUT 1.57-7.92mm (1/16"-5/16")

MOUNTING BRACKET

H 171A

Figure 79 - T.V. Cable Snap Lock

9. Road test the car, page 86. If delayed or only full throttle shifts still occur, proceed with step 10.

10. Install an oil pressure gage.
    a. Engine running and at hot idle speed.
    b. Record oil pressures in Neutral and Park.

    NOTICE: Neutral pressure should be equal to, or no more than, 69 kPa (10 p.s.i.) above Park pressure.

    c. If Neutral pressure is more than 69 kPa (10 p.s.i.) above Park pressure, proceed to step 11 below:

11. Remove the valve body cover and inspect the throttle lever and bracket assembly on the control valve pump assembly (see Figure 77). Check that the line boost lever is not distorted and not binding in the control valve pump assembly. The line boost valve must move up and down as the lifter does. Also, be sure lever spring holds the line boost lever up against the bottom of the control valve pump assembly. Make sure T.V. plunger is not stuck.

T.V. CABLE ADJUSTMENT
ADJUSTING SELF-ADJUSTING TYPE T.V. CABLE

Stop engine.

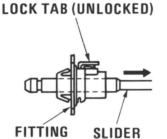

LOCK TAB (UNLOCKED)

FITTING   SLIDER

Depress lock tab and hold. Move slider back through fitting in direction away from throttle body or pump lever until slider stops against fitting.

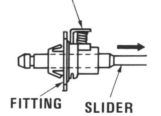

LOCK TAB (LOCKED)

FITTING   SLIDER

Release lock tab.

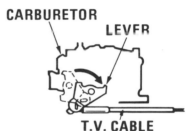

CARBURETOR   LEVER

T.V. CABLE

Open carburetor lever to "full throttle stop" position to automatically adjust T.V. cable. Release Carburetor lever.

ADJUSTING MANUAL TYPE T.V. CABLE

Stop engine.

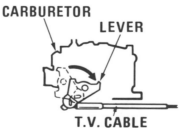

SNAP LOCK

PUSH UP TO UNLOCK

Unlock T.V. cable "snap-lock" button.

CARBURETOR   LEVER

T.V. CABLE

Rotate carburetor lever by hand to wide open throttle and hold open.

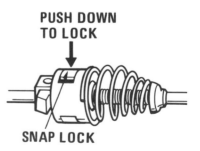

PUSH DOWN TO LOCK

SNAP LOCK

Engage T.V. cable "snap-lock" button.

ROAD TEST PROCEDURE

DRIVE RANGE:

Position selector lever in DRIVE RANGE and accelerate the vehicle. A 1-2 and 2-3 shift should occur at all throttle openings. (The shift points will vary with the throttle openings.) Check part throttle 3-2 downshift at 30 m.p.h. (50 km/h) by quickly opening throttle approximately three-fourths. At 50 m.p.h. (80 km/h) the transmission should downshift 3-2 by depressing the accelerator fully.

INTERMEDIATE RANGE:

Position the selector lever in INTERMEDIATE RANGE and accelerate the vehicle. A 1-2 shift should occur at all throttle openings. (No 2-3 shift can be obtained in this range.) The 1-2 shift point will vary with throttle opening. Check detent 2-1 downshift at 20 m.p.h. (32 km/h). The transmission should downshift 2-1. The 1-2 shift in INTERMEDIATE RANGE is somewhat firmer than in DRIVE RANGE. This is normal.

Position the selector lever in DRIVE RANGE, and with the vehicle speed at approximately 50 m.p.h. (80 km/h), with closed or 0 throttle, move the selector lever to INTERMEDIATE RANGE. The transmission should downshift to 2nd. An increase in engine r.p.m. and an engine braking effect should be noticed.

LO RANGE:

Position the selector lever in LO RANGE and accelerate the vehicle. No upshift should occur in this range.

LO RANGE:
OVERRUN BRAKING:

At 40 m.p.h. (64 km/h), with throttle closed, move the selector lever to LO. A 2-1 downshift should occur in the speed range of approximately 40 to 25 m.p.h. (64 to 40 km/h), depending on valve body calibration. The 2-1 downshift at closed throttle will be accompanied by increased engine r.p.m. and an engine braking effect should be noticed. Stop vehicle.

REVERSE RANGE:

Position the selector lever in REVERSE POSITION and check for reverse operation.

USE THE OIL PRESSURE GAGE-

Refer To Page 98 If Oil Pressures Are High Or Low

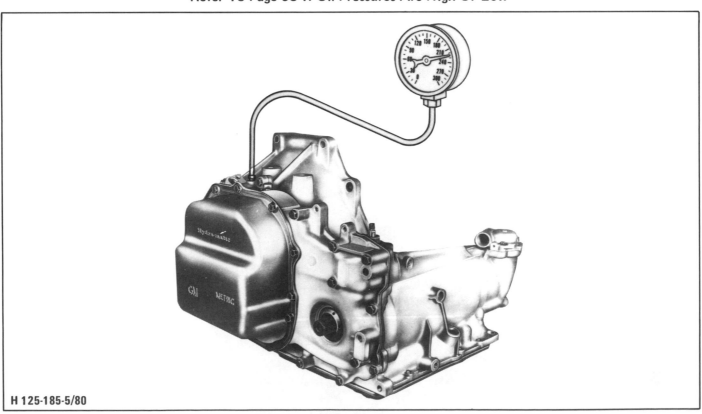

H 125-185-5/80

Figure 80 - Oil Pressure Gage Installed

PRELIMINARY CHECK PROCEDURE

CHECK TRANSMISSION OIL LEVEL, PAGE 82
CHECK AND ADJUST T.V. CABLE, PAGE 85
CHECK OUTSIDE MANUAL LINKAGE AND CORRECT, PAGE 83
CHECK ENGINE TUNE
INSTALL OIL PRESSURE GAGE, PAGE 86
CONNECT TACHOMETER TO ENGINE

CHECK OIL PRESSURES IN THE FOLLOWING MANNER:

Minimum T.V. Line Pressure Check
Set the T.V. cable to specification; and with the brakes applied, take the line pressure readings in the ranges and at the engine r.p.m.'s indicated in the chart below.

Full T.V. Line Pressure Check
Full T.V. line pressure readings are obtained by tying or holding the T.V. cable to the full extent of its travel; and with the brakes applied, take the line pressure readings in the ranges and at the engine r.p.m.'s indicated in the chart below.

NOTICE   Total running time for this combination not to exceed 2 minutes.

CAUTION   Brakes must be applied at all times.

MODEL	RANGE	NORMAL OIL PRESSURE AT MINIMUM T.V.		NORMAL OIL PRESSURE AT FULL T.V.	
		kPa	P.S.I.	kPa	P.S.I.
PZ, CV	Park at 1,000 RPM	480 - 620	70 - 90	No T.V. pressure in Park. Line pressure is the same as Park at minimum T.V.	
PZ CV	Reverse at 1,000 RPM	830 - 1100 830 - 1100	120 - 160 120 - 160	1480 - 1895 1725 - 2135	215 - 275 250 - 310
PZ CV	Neutral at 1,000 RPM	480 - 620 480 - 620	70 - 90 70 - 90	830 - 1100 965 - 1240	120 - 160 140 - 180
PZ CV	Drive at 1,000 RPM	Same as Neutral		Same as Neutral	
PZ, CV	Intermediate at 1,000 RPM	860 - 1070	125 - 155	860 - 1070	125 - 155
PZ, CV	Lo at 1,000 RPM	Same as Intermediate		No T.V. pressure in Lo Range. Line Pressure is the same as Intermediate at minimum T.V.	

Line pressure is basically controlled by pump output and the pressure regulator valve. In addition, line pressure is boosted in Reverse, Intermediate and Lo by the reverse boost valve.

Also, in the Neutral, Drive and Reverse positions of the selector lever, the line pressure should increase with throttle opening because of the T.V. system. The T.V. system is controlled by the T.V. cable, the throttle lever and bracket assembly and the T.V. link, as well as the control valve pump assembly.

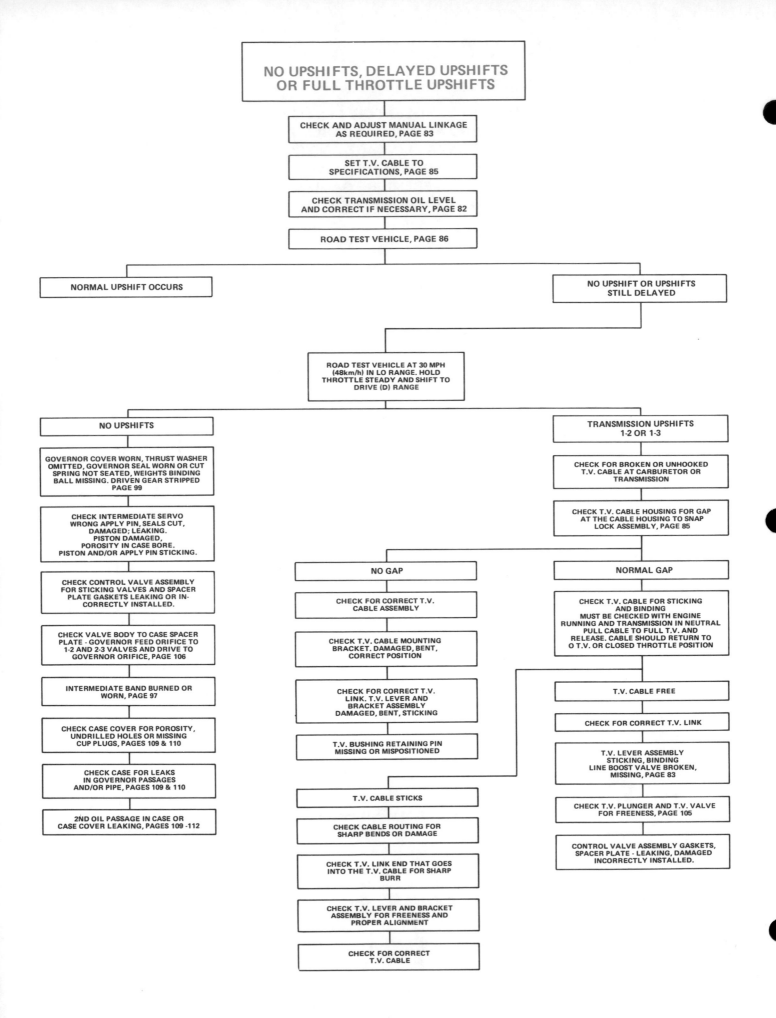

NO UPSHIFTS, DELAYED UPSHIFTS OR FULL THROTTLE UPSHIFTS

CHECK AND ADJUST MANUAL LINKAGE AS REQUIRED, PAGE 83

SET T.V. CABLE TO SPECIFICATIONS, PAGE 85

CHECK TRANSMISSION OIL LEVEL AND CORRECT IF NECESSARY, PAGE 82

ROAD TEST VEHICLE, PAGE 86

NORMAL UPSHIFT OCCURS

NO UPSHIFT OR UPSHIFTS STILL DELAYED

ROAD TEST VEHICLE AT 30 MPH (48km/h) IN LO RANGE. HOLD THROTTLE STEADY AND SHIFT TO DRIVE (D) RANGE

NO UPSHIFTS

GOVERNOR COVER WORN, THRUST WASHER OMITTED, GOVERNOR SEAL WORN OR CUT SPRING NOT SEATED, WEIGHTS BINDING BALL MISSING. DRIVEN GEAR STRIPPED PAGE 99

CHECK INTERMEDIATE SERVO WRONG APPLY PIN, SEALS CUT, DAMAGED; LEAKING. PISTON DAMAGED, POROSITY IN CASE BORE. PISTON AND/OR APPLY PIN STICKING.

CHECK CONTROL VALVE ASSEMBLY FOR STICKING VALVES AND SPACER PLATE GASKETS LEAKING OR IN-CORRECTLY INSTALLED.

CHECK VALVE BODY TO CASE SPACER PLATE - GOVERNOR FEED ORIFICE TO 1-2 AND 2-3 VALVES AND DRIVE TO GOVERNOR ORIFICE, PAGE 106

INTERMEDIATE BAND BURNED OR WORN, PAGE 97

CHECK CASE COVER FOR POROSITY, UNDRILLED HOLES OR MISSING CUP PLUGS, PAGES 109 & 110

CHECK CASE FOR LEAKS IN GOVERNOR PASSAGES AND/OR PIPE, PAGES 109 & 110

2ND OIL PASSAGE IN CASE OR CASE COVER LEAKING, PAGES 109 -112

TRANSMISSION UPSHIFTS 1-2 OR 1-3

CHECK FOR BROKEN OR UNHOOKED T.V. CABLE AT CARBURETOR OR TRANSMISSION

CHECK T.V. CABLE HOUSING FOR GAP AT THE CABLE HOUSING TO SNAP LOCK ASSEMBLY, PAGE 85

NO GAP

CHECK FOR CORRECT T.V. CABLE ASSEMBLY

CHECK T.V. CABLE MOUNTING BRACKET. DAMAGED, BENT, CORRECT POSITION

CHECK FOR CORRECT T.V. LINK. T.V. LEVER AND BRACKET ASSEMBLY DAMAGED, BENT, STICKING

T.V. BUSHING RETAINING PIN MISSING OR MISPOSITIONED

T.V. CABLE STICKS

CHECK CABLE ROUTING FOR SHARP BENDS OR DAMAGE

CHECK T.V. LINK END THAT GOES INTO THE T.V. CABLE FOR SHARP BURR

CHECK T.V. LEVER AND BRACKET ASSEMBLY FOR FREENESS AND PROPER ALIGNMENT

CHECK FOR CORRECT T.V. CABLE

NORMAL GAP

CHECK T.V. CABLE FOR STICKING AND BINDING MUST BE CHECKED WITH ENGINE RUNNING AND TRANSMISSION IN NEUTRAL PULL CABLE TO FULL T.V. AND RELEASE. CABLE SHOULD RETURN TO O T.V. OR CLOSED THROTTLE POSITION

T.V. CABLE FREE

CHECK FOR CORRECT T.V. LINK

T.V. LEVER ASSEMBLY STICKING, BINDING LINE BOOST VALVE BROKEN, MISSING, PAGE 83

CHECK T.V. PLUNGER AND T.V. VALVE FOR FREENESS, PAGE 105

CONTROL VALVE ASSEMBLY GASKETS, SPACER PLATE - LEAKING, DAMAGED INCORRECTLY INSTALLED.

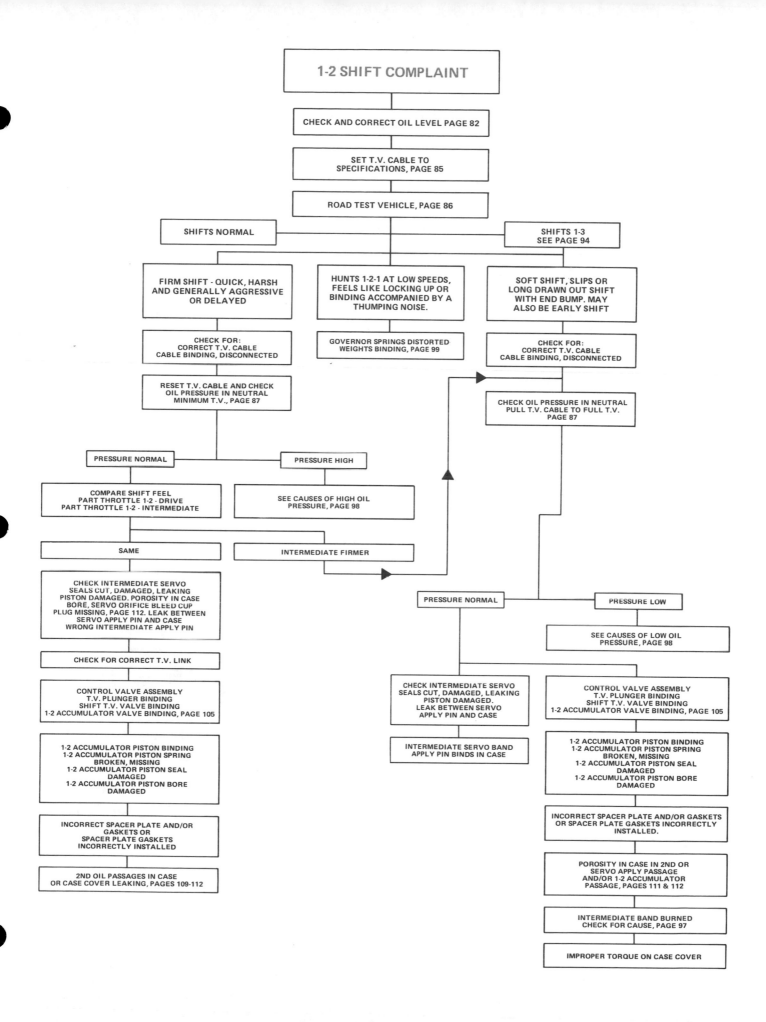

1-2 SHIFT COMPLAINT

CHECK AND CORRECT OIL LEVEL PAGE 82

SET T.V. CABLE TO SPECIFICATIONS, PAGE 85

ROAD TEST VEHICLE, PAGE 86

SHIFTS NORMAL

SHIFTS 1-3 SEE PAGE 94

FIRM SHIFT - QUICK, HARSH AND GENERALLY AGGRESSIVE OR DELAYED

HUNTS 1-2-1 AT LOW SPEEDS, FEELS LIKE LOCKING UP OR BINDING ACCOMPANIED BY A THUMPING NOISE.

SOFT SHIFT, SLIPS OR LONG DRAWN OUT SHIFT WITH END BUMP. MAY ALSO BE EARLY SHIFT

CHECK FOR: CORRECT T.V. CABLE CABLE BINDING, DISCONNECTED

GOVERNOR SPRINGS DISTORTED WEIGHTS BINDING, PAGE 99

CHECK FOR: CORRECT T.V. CABLE CABLE BINDING, DISCONNECTED

RESET T.V. CABLE AND CHECK OIL PRESSURE IN NEUTRAL MINIMUM T.V., PAGE 87

CHECK OIL PRESSURE IN NEUTRAL PULL T.V. CABLE TO FULL T.V. PAGE 87

PRESSURE NORMAL

PRESSURE HIGH

COMPARE SHIFT FEEL PART THROTTLE 1-2 - DRIVE PART THROTTLE 1-2 - INTERMEDIATE

SEE CAUSES OF HIGH OIL PRESSURE, PAGE 98

SAME

INTERMEDIATE FIRMER

PRESSURE NORMAL

PRESSURE LOW

CHECK INTERMEDIATE SERVO SEALS CUT, DAMAGED, LEAKING PISTON DAMAGED. POROSITY IN CASE BORE, SERVO ORIFICE BLEED CUP PLUG MISSING, PAGE 112. LEAK BETWEEN SERVO APPLY PIN AND CASE WRONG INTERMEDIATE APPLY PIN

SEE CAUSES OF LOW OIL PRESSURE, PAGE 98

CHECK FOR CORRECT T.V. LINK

CHECK INTERMEDIATE SERVO SEALS CUT, DAMAGED, LEAKING PISTON DAMAGED. LEAK BETWEEN SERVO APPLY PIN AND CASE

CONTROL VALVE ASSEMBLY T.V. PLUNGER BINDING SHIFT T.V. VALVE BINDING 1-2 ACCUMULATOR VALVE BINDING, PAGE 105

CONTROL VALVE ASSEMBLY T.V. PLUNGER BINDING SHIFT T.V. VALVE BINDING 1-2 ACCUMULATOR VALVE BINDING, PAGE 105

INTERMEDIATE SERVO BAND APPLY PIN BINDS IN CASE

1-2 ACCUMULATOR PISTON BINDING 1-2 ACCUMULATOR PISTON SPRING BROKEN, MISSING 1-2 ACCUMULATOR PISTON SEAL DAMAGED 1-2 ACCUMULATOR PISTON BORE DAMAGED

1-2 ACCUMULATOR PISTON BINDING 1-2 ACCUMULATOR PISTON SPRING BROKEN, MISSING 1-2 ACCUMULATOR PISTON SEAL DAMAGED 1-2 ACCUMULATOR PISTON BORE DAMAGED

INCORRECT SPACER PLATE AND/OR GASKETS OR SPACER PLATE GASKETS INCORRECTLY INSTALLED

INCORRECT SPACER PLATE AND/OR GASKETS OR SPACER PLATE GASKETS INCORRECTLY INSTALLED.

2ND OIL PASSAGES IN CASE OR CASE COVER LEAKING, PAGES 109-112

POROSITY IN CASE IN 2ND OR SERVO APPLY PASSAGE AND/OR 1-2 ACCUMULATOR PASSAGE, PAGES 111 & 112

INTERMEDIATE BAND BURNED CHECK FOR CAUSE, PAGE 97

IMPROPER TORQUE ON CASE COVER

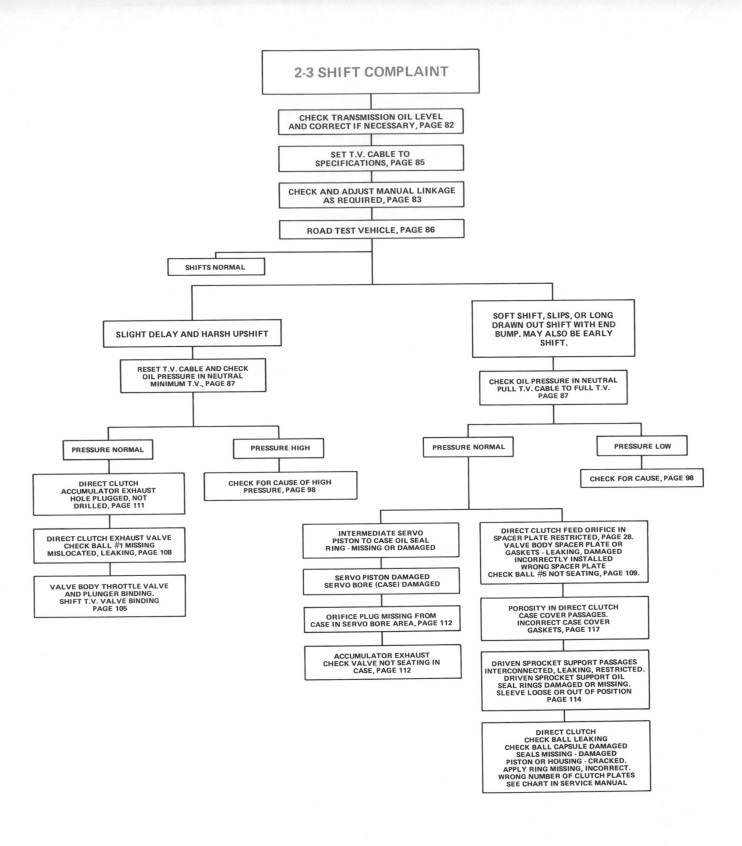

2-3 SHIFT COMPLAINT

CHECK TRANSMISSION OIL LEVEL AND CORRECT IF NECESSARY, PAGE 82

SET T.V. CABLE TO SPECIFICATIONS, PAGE 85

CHECK AND ADJUST MANUAL LINKAGE AS REQUIRED, PAGE 83

ROAD TEST VEHICLE, PAGE 86

SHIFTS NORMAL

SLIGHT DELAY AND HARSH UPSHIFT

SOFT SHIFT, SLIPS, OR LONG DRAWN OUT SHIFT WITH END BUMP. MAY ALSO BE EARLY SHIFT.

RESET T.V. CABLE AND CHECK OIL PRESSURE IN NEUTRAL MINIMUM T.V., PAGE 87

CHECK OIL PRESSURE IN NEUTRAL PULL T.V. CABLE TO FULL T.V. PAGE 87

PRESSURE NORMAL

PRESSURE HIGH

PRESSURE NORMAL

PRESSURE LOW

DIRECT CLUTCH ACCUMULATOR EXHAUST HOLE PLUGGED, NOT DRILLED, PAGE 111

CHECK FOR CAUSE OF HIGH PRESSURE, PAGE 98

CHECK FOR CAUSE, PAGE 98

DIRECT CLUTCH EXHAUST VALVE CHECK BALL #1 MISSING MISLOCATED, LEAKING, PAGE 108

VALVE BODY THROTTLE VALVE AND PLUNGER BINDING. SHIFT T.V. VALVE BINDING PAGE 105

INTERMEDIATE SERVO PISTON TO CASE OIL SEAL RING - MISSING OR DAMAGED

DIRECT CLUTCH FEED ORIFICE IN SPACER PLATE RESTRICTED, PAGE 28. VALVE BODY SPACER PLATE OR GASKETS - LEAKING, DAMAGED INCORRECTLY INSTALLED WRONG SPACER PLATE CHECK BALL #5 NOT SEATING, PAGE 109.

SERVO PISTON DAMAGED SERVO BORE (CASE) DAMAGED

ORIFICE PLUG MISSING FROM CASE IN SERVO BORE AREA, PAGE 112

POROSITY IN DIRECT CLUTCH CASE COVER PASSAGES. INCORRECT CASE COVER GASKETS, PAGE 117

ACCUMULATOR EXHAUST CHECK VALVE NOT SEATING IN CASE, PAGE 112

DRIVEN SPROCKET SUPPORT PASSAGES INTERCONNECTED, LEAKING, RESTRICTED. DRIVEN SPROCKET SUPPORT OIL SEAL RINGS DAMAGED OR MISSING. SLEEVE LOOSE OR OUT OF POSITION PAGE 114

DIRECT CLUTCH CHECK BALL LEAKING CHECK BALL CAPSULE DAMAGED SEALS MISSING - DAMAGED PISTON OR HOUSING - CRACKED. APPLY RING MISSING, INCORRECT. WRONG NUMBER OF CLUTCH PLATES SEE CHART IN SERVICE MANUAL

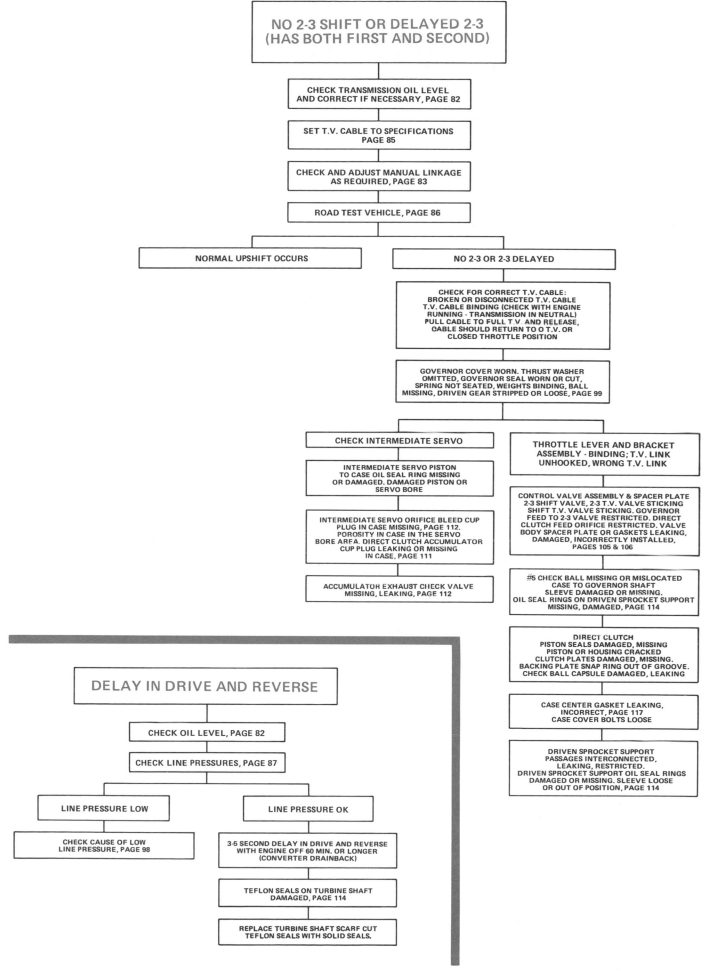

**NO 2-3 SHIFT OR DELAYED 2-3
(HAS BOTH FIRST AND SECOND)**

CHECK TRANSMISSION OIL LEVEL
AND CORRECT IF NECESSARY, PAGE 82

SET T.V. CABLE TO SPECIFICATIONS
PAGE 85

CHECK AND ADJUST MANUAL LINKAGE
AS REQUIRED, PAGE 83

ROAD TEST VEHICLE, PAGE 86

NORMAL UPSHIFT OCCURS

NO 2-3 OR 2-3 DELAYED

CHECK FOR CORRECT T.V. CABLE:
BROKEN OR DISCONNECTED T.V. CABLE
T.V. CABLE BINDING (CHECK WITH ENGINE
RUNNING - TRANSMISSION IN NEUTRAL)
PULL CABLE TO FULL T.V. AND RELEASE,
CABLE SHOULD RETURN TO O T.V. OR
CLOSED THROTTLE POSITION

GOVERNOR COVER WORN. THRUST WASHER
OMITTED, GOVERNOR SEAL WORN OR CUT,
SPRING NOT SEATED, WEIGHTS BINDING, BALL
MISSING, DRIVEN GEAR STRIPPED OR LOOSE, PAGE 99

CHECK INTERMEDIATE SERVO

THROTTLE LEVER AND BRACKET
ASSEMBLY - BINDING; T.V. LINK
UNHOOKED, WRONG T.V. LINK

INTERMEDIATE SERVO PISTON
TO CASE OIL SEAL RING MISSING
OR DAMAGED. DAMAGED PISTON OR
SERVO BORE

CONTROL VALVE ASSEMBLY & SPACER PLATE
2-3 SHIFT VALVE, 2-3 T.V. VALVE STICKING
SHIFT T.V. VALVE STICKING. GOVERNOR
FEED TO 2-3 VALVE RESTRICTED. DIRECT
CLUTCH FEED ORIFICE RESTRICTED. VALVE
BODY SPACER PLATE OR GASKETS LEAKING,
DAMAGED, INCORRECTLY INSTALLED,
PAGES 105 & 106

INTERMEDIATE SERVO ORIFICE BLEED CUP
PLUG IN CASE MISSING, PAGE 112.
POROSITY IN CASE IN THE SERVO
BORE AREA. DIRECT CLUTCH ACCUMULATOR
CUP PLUG LEAKING OR MISSING
IN CASE, PAGE 111

#5 CHECK BALL MISSING OR MISLOCATED
CASE TO GOVERNOR SHAFT
SLEEVE DAMAGED OR MISSING.
OIL SEAL RINGS ON DRIVEN SPROCKET SUPPORT
MISSING, DAMAGED, PAGE 114

ACCUMULATOR EXHAUST CHECK VALVE
MISSING, LEAKING, PAGE 112

DIRECT CLUTCH
PISTON SEALS DAMAGED, MISSING
PISTON OR HOUSING CRACKED
CLUTCH PLATES DAMAGED, MISSING.
BACKING PLATE SNAP RING OUT OF GROOVE.
CHECK BALL CAPSULE DAMAGED, LEAKING

CASE CENTER GASKET LEAKING,
INCORRECT, PAGE 117
CASE COVER BOLTS LOOSE

DRIVEN SPROCKET SUPPORT
PASSAGES INTERCONNECTED,
LEAKING, RESTRICTED.
DRIVEN SPROCKET SUPPORT OIL SEAL RINGS
DAMAGED OR MISSING. SLEEVE LOOSE
OR OUT OF POSITION, PAGE 114

DELAY IN DRIVE AND REVERSE

CHECK OIL LEVEL, PAGE 82

CHECK LINE PRESSURES, PAGE 87

LINE PRESSURE LOW

LINE PRESSURE OK

CHECK CAUSE OF LOW
LINE PRESSURE, PAGE 98

3-5 SECOND DELAY IN DRIVE AND REVERSE
WITH ENGINE OFF 60 MIN. OR LONGER
(CONVERTER DRAINBACK)

TEFLON SEALS ON TURBINE SHAFT
DAMAGED, PAGE 114

REPLACE TURBINE SHAFT SCARF CUT
TEFLON SEALS WITH SOLID SEALS.

NO DRIVE

A "NO DRIVE" COMPLAINT CAN BE REPORTED UNDER
SEVERAL CONDITIONS OR IN DIFFERENT OPERATING RANGES.
SELECT FROM THE FOLLOWING CONDITIONS THE ONE THAT
BEST REPRESENTS THE PROBLEM.

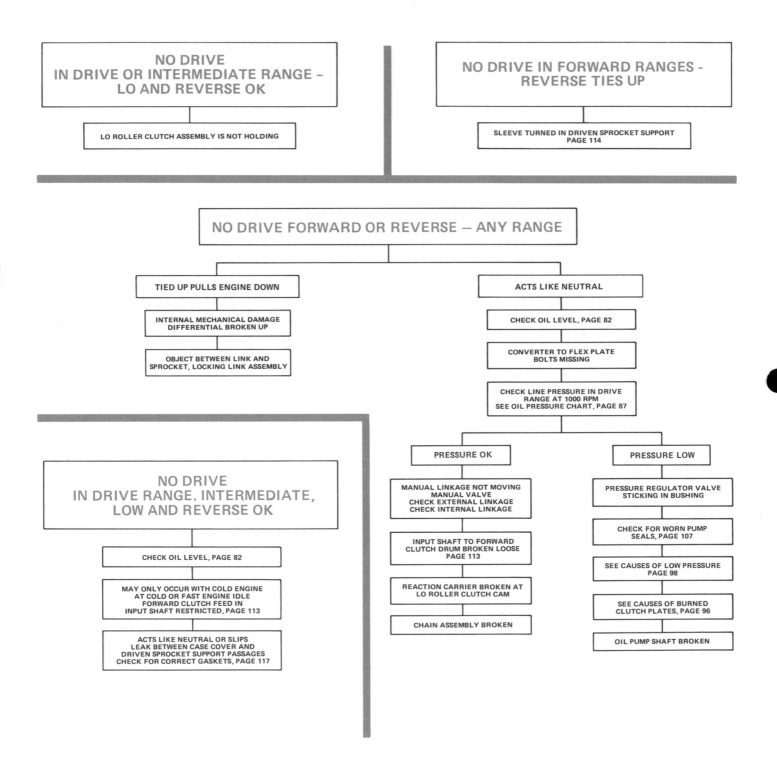

NO DRIVE
IN DRIVE OR INTERMEDIATE RANGE –
LO AND REVERSE OK

LO ROLLER CLUTCH ASSEMBLY IS NOT HOLDING

NO DRIVE IN FORWARD RANGES -
REVERSE TIES UP

SLEEVE TURNED IN DRIVEN SPROCKET SUPPORT
PAGE 114

NO DRIVE FORWARD OR REVERSE — ANY RANGE

TIED UP PULLS ENGINE DOWN

INTERNAL MECHANICAL DAMAGE
DIFFERENTIAL BROKEN UP

OBJECT BETWEEN LINK AND
SPROCKET, LOCKING LINK ASSEMBLY

ACTS LIKE NEUTRAL

CHECK OIL LEVEL, PAGE 82

CONVERTER TO FLEX PLATE
BOLTS MISSING

CHECK LINE PRESSURE IN DRIVE
RANGE AT 1000 RPM
SEE OIL PRESSURE CHART, PAGE 87

PRESSURE OK

MANUAL LINKAGE NOT MOVING
MANUAL VALVE
CHECK EXTERNAL LINKAGE
CHECK INTERNAL LINKAGE

INPUT SHAFT TO FORWARD
CLUTCH DRUM BROKEN LOOSE
PAGE 113

REACTION CARRIER BROKEN AT
LO ROLLER CLUTCH CAM

CHAIN ASSEMBLY BROKEN

PRESSURE LOW

PRESSURE REGULATOR VALVE
STICKING IN BUSHING

CHECK FOR WORN PUMP
SEALS, PAGE 107

SEE CAUSES OF LOW PRESSURE
PAGE 98

SEE CAUSES OF BURNED
CLUTCH PLATES, PAGE 96

OIL PUMP SHAFT BROKEN

NO DRIVE
IN DRIVE RANGE. INTERMEDIATE,
LOW AND REVERSE OK

CHECK OIL LEVEL, PAGE 82

MAY ONLY OCCUR WITH COLD ENGINE
AT COLD OR FAST ENGINE IDLE
FORWARD CLUTCH FEED IN
INPUT SHAFT RESTRICTED, PAGE 113

ACTS LIKE NEUTRAL OR SLIPS
LEAK BETWEEN CASE COVER AND
DRIVEN SPROCKET SUPPORT PASSAGES
CHECK FOR CORRECT GASKETS, PAGE 117

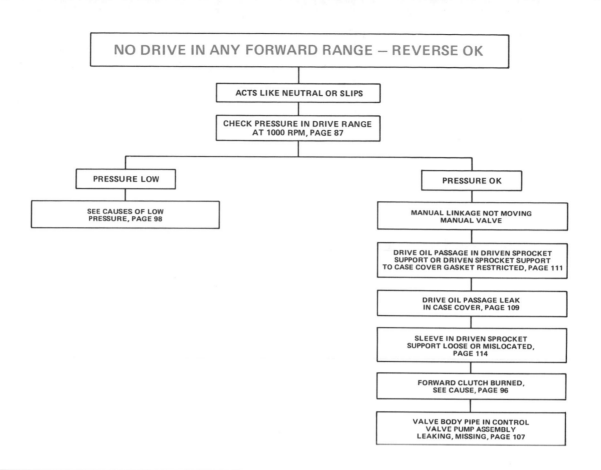

NO DRIVE IN ANY FORWARD RANGE — REVERSE OK

ACTS LIKE NEUTRAL OR SLIPS

CHECK PRESSURE IN DRIVE RANGE
AT 1000 RPM, PAGE 87

PRESSURE LOW

SEE CAUSES OF LOW
PRESSURE, PAGE 98

PRESSURE OK

MANUAL LINKAGE NOT MOVING
MANUAL VALVE

DRIVE OIL PASSAGE IN DRIVEN SPROCKET
SUPPORT OR DRIVEN SPROCKET SUPPORT
TO CASE COVER GASKET RESTRICTED, PAGE 111

DRIVE OIL PASSAGE LEAK
IN CASE COVER, PAGE 109

SLEEVE IN DRIVEN SPROCKET
SUPPORT LOOSE OR MISLOCATED,
PAGE 114

FORWARD CLUTCH BURNED,
SEE CAUSE, PAGE 96

VALVE BODY PIPE IN CONTROL
VALVE PUMP ASSEMBLY
LEAKING, MISSING, PAGE 107

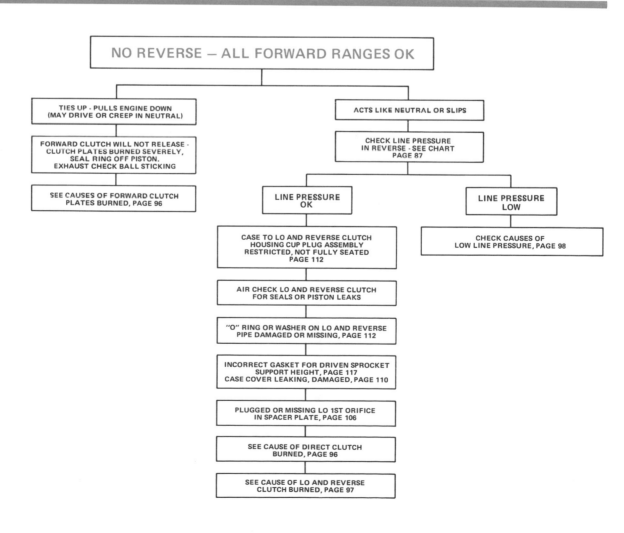

NO REVERSE — ALL FORWARD RANGES OK

TIES UP - PULLS ENGINE DOWN
(MAY DRIVE OR CREEP IN NEUTRAL)

FORWARD CLUTCH WILL NOT RELEASE -
CLUTCH PLATES BURNED SEVERELY,
SEAL RING OFF PISTON.
EXHAUST CHECK BALL STICKING

SEE CAUSES OF FORWARD CLUTCH
PLATES BURNED, PAGE 96

ACTS LIKE NEUTRAL OR SLIPS

CHECK LINE PRESSURE
IN REVERSE - SEE CHART
PAGE 87

LINE PRESSURE OK

CASE TO LO AND REVERSE CLUTCH
HOUSING CUP PLUG ASSEMBLY
RESTRICTED, NOT FULLY SEATED
PAGE 112

AIR CHECK LO AND REVERSE CLUTCH
FOR SEALS OR PISTON LEAKS

"O" RING OR WASHER ON LO AND REVERSE
PIPE DAMAGED OR MISSING, PAGE 112

INCORRECT GASKET FOR DRIVEN SPROCKET
SUPPORT HEIGHT, PAGE 117
CASE COVER LEAKING, DAMAGED, PAGE 110

PLUGGED OR MISSING LO 1ST ORIFICE
IN SPACER PLATE, PAGE 106

SEE CAUSE OF DIRECT CLUTCH
BURNED, PAGE 96

SEE CAUSE OF LO AND REVERSE
CLUTCH BURNED, PAGE 97

LINE PRESSURE LOW

CHECK CAUSES OF
LOW LINE PRESSURE, PAGE 98

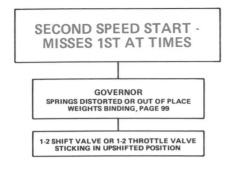

SECOND SPEED START - MISSES 1ST AT TIMES

GOVERNOR
SPRINGS DISTORTED OR OUT OF PLACE
WEIGHTS BINDING, PAGE 99

1-2 SHIFT VALVE OR 1-2 THROTTLE VALVE
STICKING IN UPSHIFTED POSITION

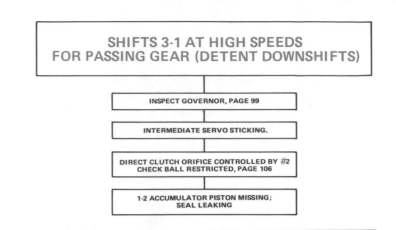

SHIFTS 3-1 AT HIGH SPEEDS FOR PASSING GEAR (DETENT DOWNSHIFTS)

INSPECT GOVERNOR, PAGE 99

INTERMEDIATE SERVO STICKING.

DIRECT CLUTCH ORIFICE CONTROLLED BY #2
CHECK BALL RESTRICTED, PAGE 106

1-2 ACCUMULATOR PISTON MISSING;
SEAL LEAKING

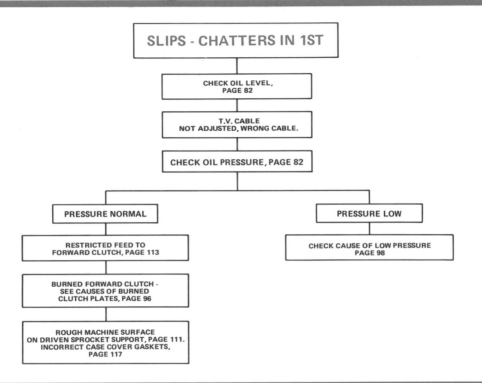

SLIPS - CHATTERS IN 1ST

CHECK OIL LEVEL,
PAGE 82

T.V. CABLE
NOT ADJUSTED, WRONG CABLE.

CHECK OIL PRESSURE, PAGE 82

PRESSURE NORMAL

RESTRICTED FEED TO
FORWARD CLUTCH, PAGE 113

BURNED FORWARD CLUTCH -
SEE CAUSES OF BURNED
CLUTCH PLATES, PAGE 96

ROUGH MACHINE SURFACE
ON DRIVEN SPROCKET SUPPORT, PAGE 111.
INCORRECT CASE COVER GASKETS,
PAGE 117

PRESSURE LOW

CHECK CAUSE OF LOW PRESSURE
PAGE 98

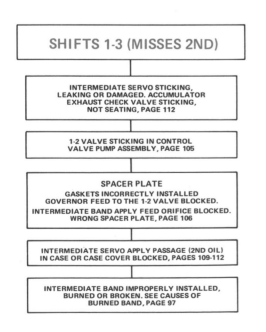

SHIFTS 1-3 (MISSES 2ND)

INTERMEDIATE SERVO STICKING,
LEAKING OR DAMAGED. ACCUMULATOR
EXHAUST CHECK VALVE STICKING,
NOT SEATING, PAGE 112

1-2 VALVE STICKING IN CONTROL
VALVE PUMP ASSEMBLY, PAGE 105

SPACER PLATE
GASKETS INCORRECTLY INSTALLED
GOVERNOR FEED TO THE 1-2 VALVE BLOCKED.
INTERMEDIATE BAND APPLY FEED ORIFICE BLOCKED.
WRONG SPACER PLATE, PAGE 106

INTERMEDIATE SERVO APPLY PASSAGE (2ND OIL)
IN CASE OR CASE COVER BLOCKED, PAGES 109-112

INTERMEDIATE BAND IMPROPERLY INSTALLED,
BURNED OR BROKEN. SEE CAUSES OF
BURNED BAND, PAGE 97

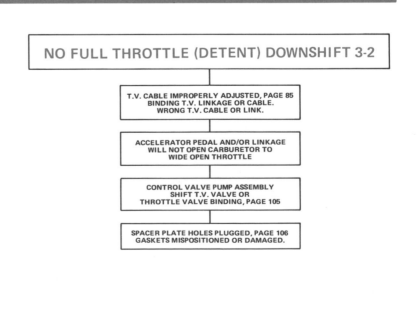

NO FULL THROTTLE (DETENT) DOWNSHIFT 3-2

T.V. CABLE IMPROPERLY ADJUSTED, PAGE 85
BINDING T.V. LINKAGE OR CABLE.
WRONG T.V. CABLE OR LINK.

ACCELERATOR PEDAL AND/OR LINKAGE
WILL NOT OPEN CARBURETOR TO
WIDE OPEN THROTTLE

CONTROL VALVE PUMP ASSEMBLY
SHIFT T.V. VALVE OR
THROTTLE VALVE BINDING, PAGE 105

SPACER PLATE HOLES PLUGGED, PAGE 106
GASKETS MISPOSITIONED OR DAMAGED.

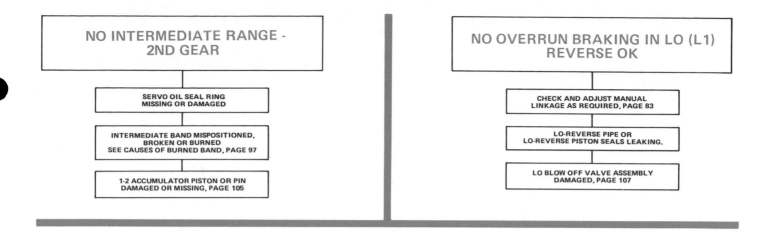

NO INTERMEDIATE RANGE - 2ND GEAR

- SERVO OIL SEAL RING MISSING OR DAMAGED
- INTERMEDIATE BAND MISPOSITIONED, BROKEN OR BURNED SEE CAUSES OF BURNED BAND, PAGE 97
- 1-2 ACCUMULATOR PISTON OR PIN DAMAGED OR MISSING, PAGE 105

NO OVERRUN BRAKING IN LO (L1) REVERSE OK

- CHECK AND ADJUST MANUAL LINKAGE AS REQUIRED, PAGE 83
- LO-REVERSE PIPE OR LO-REVERSE PISTON SEALS LEAKING.
- LO BLOW OFF VALVE ASSEMBLY DAMAGED, PAGE 107

CAUTION: BEFORE CHECKING TRANSMISSION FOR WHAT IS BELIEVED TO BE "TRANS. NOISE," MAKE CERTAIN THE NOISE IS NOT FROM THE WATER PUMP, ALTERNATOR, AIR CONDITIONER, POWER STEERING, ETC. THESE COMPONENTS CAN BE ISOLATED BY REMOVING THE PROPER BELT AND RUNNING THE ENGINE NOT MORE THAN TWO MINUTES AT ONE TIME.

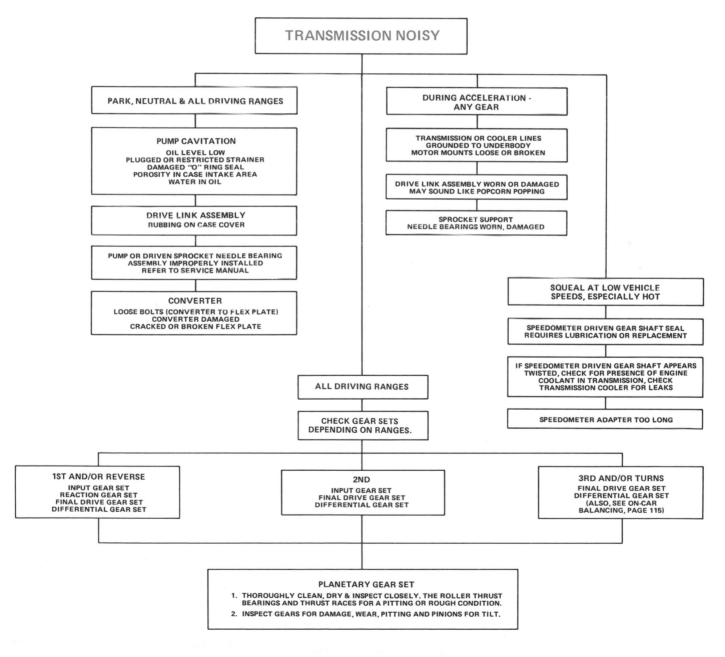

TRANSMISSION NOISY

PARK, NEUTRAL & ALL DRIVING RANGES

- PUMP CAVITATION
  OIL LEVEL LOW
  PLUGGED OR RESTRICTED STRAINER
  DAMAGED "O" RING SEAL
  POROSITY IN CASE INTAKE AREA
  WATER IN OIL
- DRIVE LINK ASSEMBLY
  RUBBING ON CASE COVER
- PUMP OR DRIVEN SPROCKET NEEDLE BEARING ASSEMBLY IMPROPERLY INSTALLED REFER TO SERVICE MANUAL
- CONVERTER
  LOOSE BOLTS (CONVERTER TO FLEX PLATE)
  CONVERTER DAMAGED
  CRACKED OR BROKEN FLEX PLATE

DURING ACCELERATION - ANY GEAR

- TRANSMISSION OR COOLER LINES GROUNDED TO UNDERBODY MOTOR MOUNTS LOOSE OR BROKEN
- DRIVE LINK ASSEMBLY WORN OR DAMAGED MAY SOUND LIKE POPCORN POPPING
- SPROCKET SUPPORT NEEDLE BEARINGS WORN, DAMAGED

SQUEAL AT LOW VEHICLE SPEEDS, ESPECIALLY HOT

- SPEEDOMETER DRIVEN GEAR SHAFT SEAL REQUIRES LUBRICATION OR REPLACEMENT
- IF SPEEDOMETER DRIVEN GEAR SHAFT APPEARS TWISTED, CHECK FOR PRESENCE OF ENGINE COOLANT IN TRANSMISSION, CHECK TRANSMISSION COOLER FOR LEAKS
- SPEEDOMETER ADAPTER TOO LONG

ALL DRIVING RANGES

- CHECK GEAR SETS DEPENDING ON RANGES.

1ST AND/OR REVERSE
INPUT GEAR SET
REACTION GEAR SET
FINAL DRIVE GEAR SET
DIFFERENTIAL GEAR SET

2ND
INPUT GEAR SET
FINAL DRIVE GEAR SET
DIFFERENTIAL GEAR SET

3RD AND/OR TURNS
FINAL DRIVE GEAR SET
DIFFERENTIAL GEAR SET
(ALSO, SEE ON-CAR BALANCING, PAGE 115)

PLANETARY GEAR SET
1. THOROUGHLY CLEAN, DRY & INSPECT CLOSELY. THE ROLLER THRUST BEARINGS AND THRUST RACES FOR A PITTING OR ROUGH CONDITION.
2. INSPECT GEARS FOR DAMAGE, WEAR, PITTING AND PINIONS FOR TILT.

CAUSES OF BURNED CLUTCH PLATES OR BAND

A burned clutch or band is generally caused by some condition such as low pressure and/or leaks that prevent proper application. During diagnosis or inspection, this cause must be found.

A cut or damaged seal may be the cause of a clutch problem or may be the result of a burned clutch. If a clutch is burned, excessive piston travel may result and allow one or more of the piston seals to come out of the bore and become cut or folded. When looking for the cause of the problem, the condition of the piston seals should be considered; but further inspection should be made to determine if some other area is the cause of the problem, to prevent a repeat problem.

EXAMPLE: A leak at an intermediate servo piston seal may be the cause of a burned direct clutch and/or intermediate band because the oil pressure that applies the direct clutch also releases the servo piston.

IN ALL CASES OF BURNED CLUTCH PLATES OR BAND — CHECK THE FOLLOWING:

1. Driven Sprocket Support
   a. Leaking (damaged) seal rings on driven sprocket support, page 114.
   b. Wrong case cover gaskets or gaskets not sealing, pages 116-117.
   c. Driven sprocket support sleeve loose or mis-positioned, page 114.
   d. Loose attaching bolts. Torque to 24N•m (18 ft.-lbs.)

2. Case Cover and Case
   a. Channels blocked or interconnected, pages 109-112.
   b. Sealing surfaces damaged or leaking.
   c. Check balls missing or out of location, page 109.
   d. Porosity.

3. Control Valve Pump Assembly
   a. Control valve pump assembly to case cover bolts loose.
   b. Sealing surface on control valve pump assembly, spacer plate, and/or gaskets damaged or leaking.
   c. Valves leaking, binding, or sticking, page 105.
   d. Channels blocked or interconnected, page 108.

If low line pressure is present, refer to possible causes, page 98.

> NOTICE: Burned clutch plates can be caused by incorrect usage of clutch plates. Engine coolant in the transmission fluid can cause severe damage to clutch plate material and result in pieces of composition material peeling off.

BURNED DIRECT CLUTCH ONLY*

1. Direct Clutch Assembly
   a. Seals cut, missing or rolled out of groove .
   b. Exhaust ball capsule in housing damaged and not sealing.
   c. Piston or housing damaged, leaking.
   d. Snap ring not fully seated.

2. Intermediate Servo Assembly
   a. Wrong servo pin - check selectivity.
   b. Seals missing or damaged.
   c. Servo bore scored or damaged.
   d. Servo orifice bleed plug missing, page 112.
   e. Band apply pin tight in case bore.

3. Case Cover and Case
   a. #5 check ball missing or off location in case cover, page 109.
   b. Accumulator exhaust check valve missing or not sealing in case, page 112.

BURNED FORWARD CLUTCH ONLY*

1. Forward Clutch Assembly
   a. Seal rings on imput shaft damaged or missing, page 113.
   b. First design input shaft thrust washer installed incorrectly.
   c. Input shaft feed passage or orifice restricted, page 113.
   d. Exhaust ball capsule in housing damaged and not sealing, page 113.
   e. Backing plate or snap ring incorrectly installed.
   f. Piston seals missing or damaged.
   g. Apply ring missing.
   h. Piston, housing, or shaft damaged, leaking.

2. Control Valve Pump Assembly
   a. Valve body pipe loose or leaking, page 107.

BURNED LO AND REVERSE CLUTCH ONLY*

1. Lo and Reverse Clutch Assembly
   a. Housing seal area damaged.
   b. Piston or seals damaged.
   c. Apply ring missing.

2. Control Valve Pump Assembly
   a. Reverse boost valve sticking, page 105.

3. Case Cover and Case
   a. #4 or #5 check ball missing or off location in case cover, page 109.

b. Lo and Reverse pipe leaking in case bore, page 112.

c. Lo and Reverse clutch housing to case cup plug assembly restricted, damaged, or not seated properly, page 112.

d. Lo and Reverse pipe to case "O" ring and/or seal backup ring damaged or missing, page 112.

BURNED INTERMEDIATE BAND ONLY*

1. Intermediate Band

   a. Band not properly installed and aligned in case.

   b. Apply pin not engaged.

2. Intermediate Servo Assembly

   a. Wrong servo pin - check selectivity.

   b. Seals missing or damaged.

c. Servo bore scored or damaged.

d. Band apply pin tight in case bore.

3. Case Cover and Case.

   a. Accumulator check valve missing or not sealing properly, page 112.

   b. Direct clutch accumulator cup plug missing, page 111.

   c. #1 or #2 check balls missing or off location, pages 109 and 110.

   d. 1-2 accumulator piston missing or seal leaking.

4. Control Valve Pump Assembly

   a. 1-2 accumulator valve sticking, page 105.

* See also above section labeled "IN ALL CASES OF BURNED CLUTCH PLATES OR BAND."

CAUSES OF OIL LEAKS

Before attempting to correct an oil leak, the actual source of the leak must be determined. In many cases, the source of the leak can be deceiving due to "wind flow" around the engine and transmission.

The suspected area should be wiped clean of all oil before inspecting for the source of the leak. Red dye is used in the transmission oil at the assembly plant and will indicate if the oil leak is from the transmission.

Oil leaks around the engine and transmission are generally carried toward the rear of the car by the air stream. For example, a transmission "oil filler tube to case leak" will sometimes appear as a leak at the rear of the transmission. In determining the source of an oil leak, two checks should be made.

1. With the engine running, check for external oil pressure leaks.

2. With the engine off, check for oil leaks due to the raised oil level caused by drainback of converter oil into the transmission.

POSSIBLE POINTS OF OIL LEAKS

1. Transmission oil pan or valve body cover leak.

   a. Attaching bolts not correctly torqued.

   b. Improperly installed or damaged gasket.

   c. Oil pan or case cover mounting face not flat.

   d. Stripped or missing bolts.

2. Case Leak

   a. Filler pipe sleeve seal damaged or missing; filler pipe bracket to engine mispositioned "loading" one side of seal.

   b. T.V. cable sleeve seal missing, damaged or improperly installed.

   c. Governor cover and "O" ring damaged or missing.

   d. Speedometer "O" ring damaged.

   e. Manual shaft lip seal damaged, missing or improperly installed.

   f. Line pressure tap plug, governor pressure plug, loose or stripped.

   g. Porous casting.

   h. Case to case cover not sealed — use Loctite 515 on both sides of case cover gasket.

   i. Cooler fittings, loose or stripped.

   j. Output shaft seals damaged, improperly installed.

   k. Stripped or missing bolts.

3. Leak at converter end of transmission.
   a. Converter seal leaks.
      1) Seal lip cut, not fully seated. Check converter hub for nicks, etc.
      2) Bushing moved forward and damaged.
      3) Garter spring missing from seal.
   b. Case to case cover bolts washer missing, damaged or threads stripped.
   c. Converter leak in weld area.
   d. Two (2) drain back holes in drive sprocket support plugged, page 114.

   e. Porous case.

4. Oil comes out vent.
   a. Transmission over-filled.
   b. Water in oil.
   c. Incorrect dipstick.
   d. Gasket off location.
   e. Case cover porosity.

CAUSES OF LOW OIL PRESSURE

1. Low oil level.

2. T.V. system (pressure low in Neutral, Drive, low to normal in Intermediate and Reverse.)
   a. T.V. cable misadjusted or sticking.
   b. T.V. linkage — binding, incorrect cable.
   c. Throttle valve stuck.
   d. Shift T.V. valve stuck.

3. Oil strainer plugged.

4. Oil strainer "O" ring seal leaking or damaged.

5. Control valve and pump assembly bolts loose.

6. Control Valve Assembly, page 105.
   a. Check ball #5 or #6, missing or out of location.
   b. Valve stuck, damaged.
      1) T.V. valve and plunger.

      2) Shift T.V. valve.
      3) Pressure regulator valve.
      4) T.V. boost valve.
      5) Pressure relief valve.
   c. 1-2 accumulator piston and/or seal — leaking or missing.
   d. Internal leaks.

7. (Lo only) Lo blow off valve damaged, #4 check ball missing — off location.

8. (Reverse only) Lo-Reverse clutch housing to case cup plug assembly leaking, page 112.

9. Pump vane broken, seals cut or missing, page 107.

10. Intermediate oil passages to pressure regulator blocked.

11. Driven sprocket support to case cover leak.

CAUSES OF HIGH OIL PRESSURE

1. T.V. system (pressure high in Neutral, Drive, normal to high in Intermediate and Reverse).
   a. T.V. cable misadjusted, sticking or broken.
   b. T.V. linkage — binding, incorrect cable.
   c. Throttle valve stuck.
   d. Shift T.V. valve stuck.
   e. T.V. lifter bent, damaged.

2. Control Valve and Pump Assembly, Page 105.
   a. Valves stuck.

   1) T.V. valve and plunger.
   2) Shift T.V. valve.
   3) Pressure regulator valve.
   4) T.V. boost valve.
   b. Pump slide stuck.

3. (Lo only) Lo blow off valve stuck closed.

4. Internal pump or case cover leaks.

GOVERNOR INSPECTION

1. Inspect the governor cover "O" ring seal for damage.

2. Inspect the governor for missing exhaust check balls.

3. Inspect the governor cover for damage or wear in its bore.

4. Inspect speedometer drive gear and thrust washer for excessive wear.

5. Inspect the governor driven gear teeth for excessive wear or damage. If excessively worn or damaged, closely inspect the governor drive gear on the output shaft for nicks or damage.

6. The governor secondary weight may be bent and cause the governor weights to bind and not have free motion. (The secondary weight is thinner and lighter than the primary weight.) There must be some clearance between the weights. If no clearance exists, carefully place a small screwdriver between the weights at the pin and pry to create enough clearance to provide free motion of the weights. (See Figure 81, Point A.) At the same time, make sure to maintain some clearance between the secondary weight and the governor shaft. (See Figure 81, Point B.)

7. The primary and secondary springs must stand straight and not be mis-positioned or tilted. If improperly positioned or tilted, position it properly using a small screwdriver.

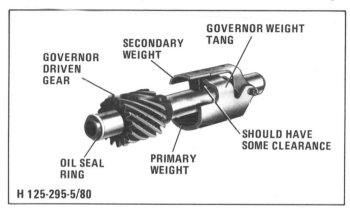

H 125-295-5/80

Figure 81 - Governor Assembly

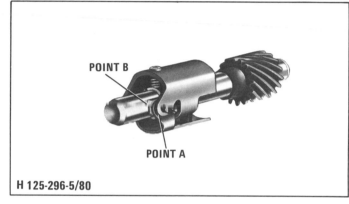

H 125-296-5/80

Figure 82 - Governor Assembly

CONVERTER STATOR OPERATION DIAGNOSIS

The torque converter stator assembly and its related roller clutch can possibly have one of two different type malfunctions; namely,

A. The stator assembly freewheels in both directions.

B. The stator assembly remains locked up at all times.

CONDITION A

If the stator roller clutch becomes ineffective, the stator assembly freewheels at all times in both directions. With this condition, the vehicle will tend to have poor acceleration from a standstill. At speeds above 30-35 m.p.h. (48-56 km/h), the vehicle may act normal. If poor acceleration problems are noted, it should first be determined that the exhaust system is not blocked, the engine is in good tune, and the transmission is in first (1st) gear when starting out.

If the engine will freely accelerate to high r.p.m., in Neutral (N), it can be assumed that the engine and exhaust system are normal. Driving the vehicle in Reverse (R) and checking for poor performance

will help determine if the stator is freewheeling at all times.

CONDITION B

If the stator assembly remains locked up at all times, the engine r.p.m. and vehicle speed will tend to be limited or restricted at high speeds. The vehicle performance when accelerating from a standstill will be normal. Engine over heating may be noted. Visual examination of the converter may reveal a blue color that will result from the overheating.

Under conditions A or B above, if the converter has been removed from the transmission, the stator roller clutch can be checked by inserting a finger* into the splined inner race of the roller clutch and trying to turn the race in both directions. The inner race should turn freely in the clockwise direction, but not turn or be very difficult to turn in the counterclockwise direction.

*Do not use the stator shaft to turn the race, as the results may be misleading.

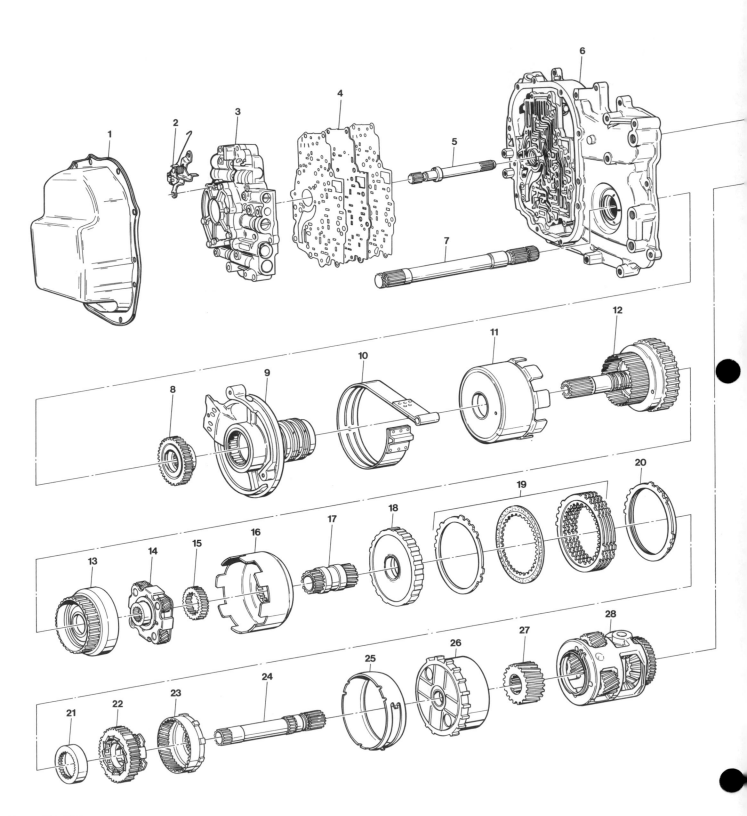

Figure 83 - Exploded View of Major Components

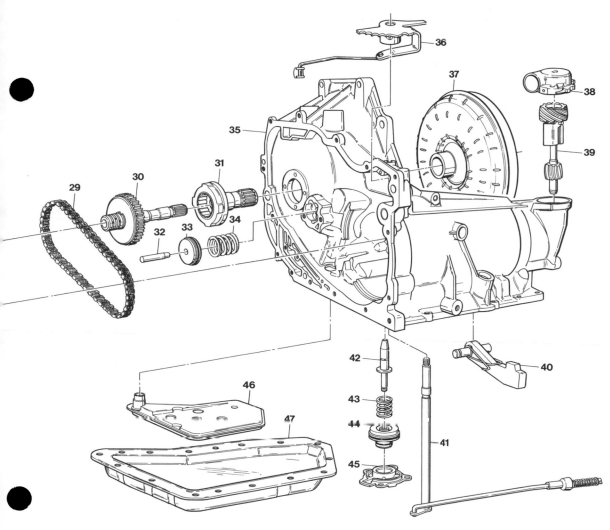

THM 125
EXPLODED VIEW OF MAJOR COMPONENTS

1. Valve Body Cover
2. Throttle Lever Bracket and Link Assembly
3. Control Valve and Oil Pump Assembly
4. Spacer Plate and Gaskets
5. Oil Pump Drive Shaft
6. Case Cover Assembly
7. Output Shaft
8. Driven Sprocket Assembly
9. Driven Sprocket Support Assembly
10. Intermediate Band Assembly
11. Direct Clutch Housing Assembly
12. Forward Clutch Housing Assembly
13. Input Internal Gear
14. Input Carrier Assembly
15. Input Sun Gear
16. Input Drum
17. Reaction Sun Gear
18. Lo and Reverse Housing Assembly
19. Lo and Reverse Clutch Plates
20. Lo and Reverse Clutch Backing Plate
21. Lo Roller Clutch Race
22. Reaction Carrier Assembly
23. Reaction Internal Gear
24. Final Drive Sun Gear Shaft

25. Final Drive Internal Gear Spacer
26. Final Drive Internal Gear
27. Final Drive Sun Gear
28. Differential Carrier Assembly
29. Drive Link Assembly
30. Drive Sprocket and Turbine Shaft Assembly
31. Drive Sprocket Support
32. 1-2 Accumulator Pin
33. 1-2 Accumulator Piston
34. 1-2 Accumulator Spring
35. Case Assembly
36. Manual Detent Lever and Rod Assembly
37. Converter Assembly
38. Governor Cover
39. Governor Assembly
40. Parking Pawl Assembly
41. Actuator Rod and Manual Shaft
42. Intermediate Band Apply Pin
43. Intermediate Servo Cushion Spring
44. Intermediate Servo Piston
45. Intermediate Servo Cover
46. Oil Strainer Assembly
47. Oil Pan

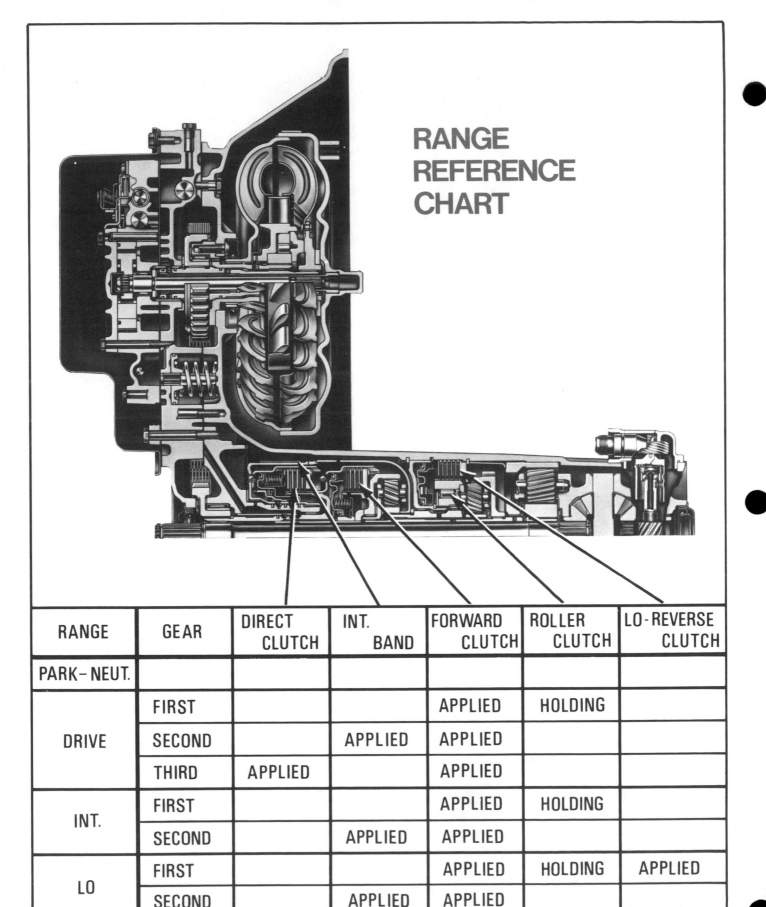

RANGE REFERENCE CHART

RANGE	GEAR	DIRECT CLUTCH	INT. BAND	FORWARD CLUTCH	ROLLER CLUTCH	LO-REVERSE CLUTCH
PARK−NEUT.						
DRIVE	FIRST			APPLIED	HOLDING	
DRIVE	SECOND		APPLIED	APPLIED		
DRIVE	THIRD	APPLIED		APPLIED		
INT.	FIRST			APPLIED	HOLDING	
INT.	SECOND		APPLIED	APPLIED		
LO	FIRST			APPLIED	HOLDING	APPLIED
LO	SECOND		APPLIED	APPLIED		
REV.		APPLIED				APPLIED

H 125-187-5/80

Figure 84 - Range Reference Chart

102

THRUST BEARING, THRUST WASHER AND BUSHING LOCATIONS

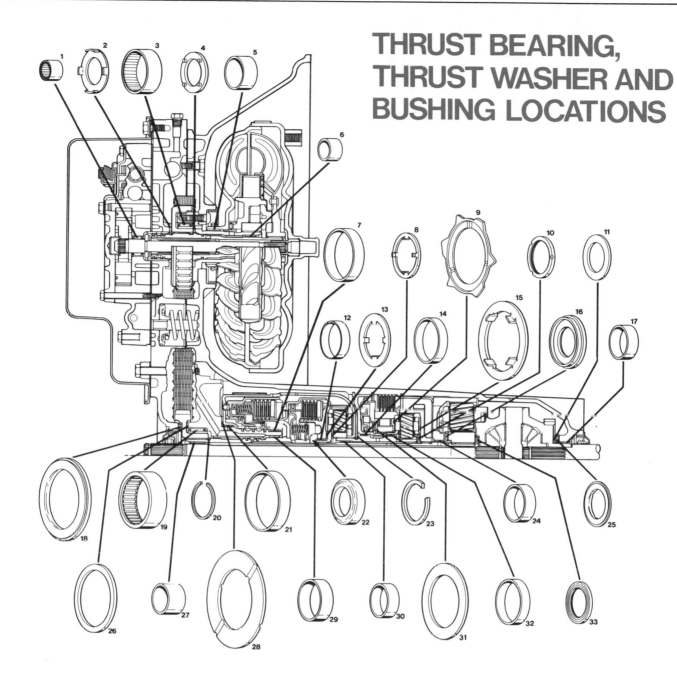

1. Pump Shaft Roller Bearing Assy.   Group 4.226
2. Case Cover To Driven Sprocket Thrust Washer   Group 4.131
3. Bearing Assembly   Group 4.131
4. Case Cover To Drive Sprocket Thrust Washer   Group 4.131
5. Converter Bushing   Group 4.115
6. Drive Sprocket Support Bushing   Group 4.226
7. Direct Clutch Drum Bushing   Group 4.169
8. Input Carrier To Input Sun Gear Thrust Washer   Group 4.159
9. Reaction Carrier to Lo Race Thrust Washer   Group 4.180
10. Reaction Sun To Internal Gear Thrust Bearing   Group 4.159
11. Differential Carrier To Case Selective Thrust Washer   Group 4.176
12. Input Internal Gear Bushing   Group 4.158
13. Input Carrier To Input Internal Gear Thrust Washer   Group 4.159
14. Lo and Reverse Clutch Housing Bushing   Group 4.159
15. Reaction Carrier To Internal Gear Thrust Washer   Group 4.180
16. Sun Gear To Internal Gear Thrust Bearing   Group 4.178
17. Case Bushing   Group 4.319

18. Driven Sprocket Thrust Bearing Assembly   Group 4.131
19. Bearing Assembly   Group 4.131
20. Selective Snap Ring   Group 4.169
21. Direct Clutch Bushing   Group 4.169
22. Input Shaft Thrust Washer   Group 4.158
23. Selective Snap Ring   Group 4.216
24. Final Drive Internal Gear Bushing   Group 4.319
25. Differential Carrier To Case Thrust Bearing Assembly   Group 4.176
26. Driven Sprocket Support Thrust Washer   Group 4.131
27. Input Shaft Bushing   Group 4.158
28. Thrust Washer   Group 4.169
29. Driven Sprocket Support Bushing   Group 4.226
30. Reaction Sun Gear Bushing   Group 4.159
31. Reverse Housing To Lo Race Selective Washer   Group 4.180
32. Reaction Carrier Bushing   Group 4.159
33. Sun Gear To Carrier Thrust Bearing   Group 4.159

H 125-287-5/80

Figure 85 - Bearing, Washer and Bushing Location

103

PARK

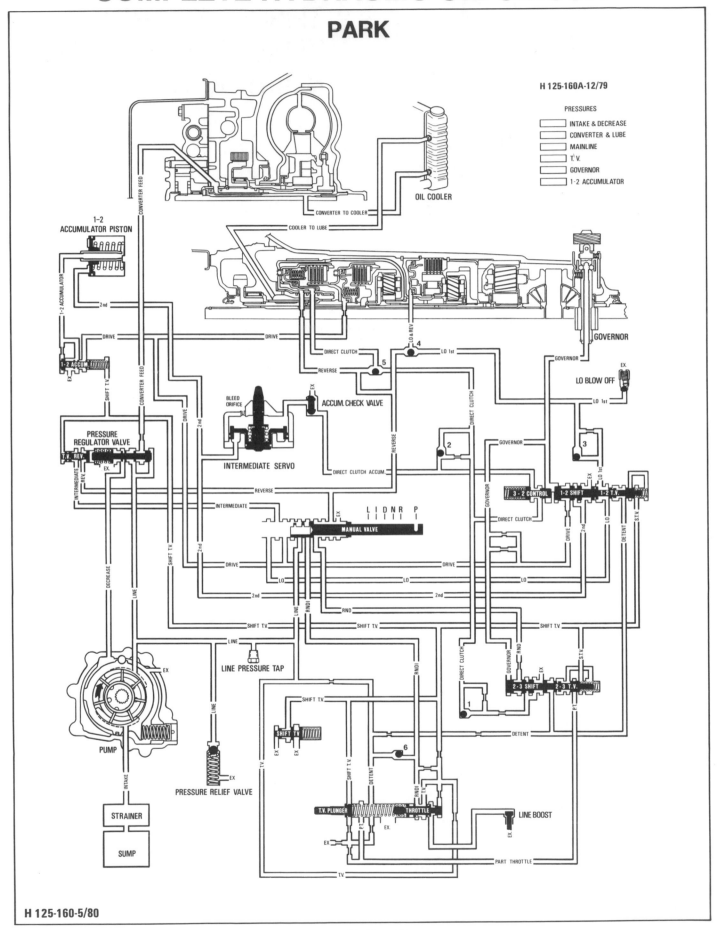

Figure 86 - Oil Flow Diagram

H 125-160-5/80

TYPICAL 125 CONTROL VALVE ASSEMBLY

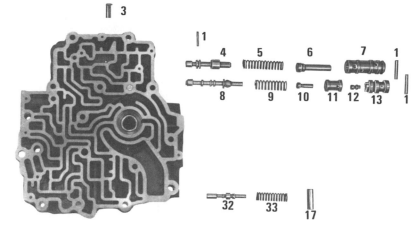

H 125-249-5/80

1. RETAINING COILED PIN
2. LINE BOOST VALVE PLUG
3. LINE BOOST VALVE
4. THROTTLE VALVE
5. THROTTLE VALVE SPRING
6. THROTTLE VALVE PLUNGER
7. T.V. PLUNGER BUSHING
8. PRESSURE REGULATOR VALVE
9. PRESSURE REGULATOR SPRING
10. REVERSE BOOST VALVE
11. REVERSE BOOST VALVE BUSHING
12. T.V. BOOST VALVE
13. T.V. BOOST VALVE BUSHING
14. VALVE BORE PLUG
15. SHIFT T.V. SPRING
16. SHIFT T.V. VALVE
17. SPRING RETAINING SLEEVE
18. PRESSURE RELIEF SPRING
19. PRESSURE RELIEF BALL
20. VALVE BORE PLUG
21. 1-2 ACCUMULATOR VALVE
22. 1-2 ACCUMULATOR BUSHING
23. 1-2 ACCUMULATOR SPRING
24. 2-3 THROTTLE VALVE BUSHING
25. 2-3 THROTTLE VALVE SPRING
26. 2-3 THROTTLE VALVE
27. 2-3 SHIFT VALVE
28. 1-2 THROTTLE VALVE BUSHING
29. 1-2 THROTTLE VALVE SPRING
30. 1-2 THROTTLE VALVE
31. 1-2 SHIFT VLAVE
32. 3-2 CONTROL VALVE
33. 3-2 VALVE SPRING
34. LO BLOW OFF BALL
35. LO BLOW OFF SPRING AND PLUG ASSEMBLY
36. LO BLOW OFF VALVE PLUG

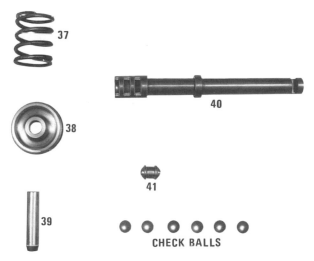

H 125-250-5/80

(Located in Case Cover)
37. 1-2 ACCUMULATOR PISTON SPRING
38. 1-2 ACCUMULATOR PISTON
39. 1-2 ACCUMULATOR PIN
40. MANUAL VALVE
   (Located in Case)
41. ACCUMULATOR EXHAUST CHECK VALVE

CHECK BALLS

1. DIRECT CLUTCH EXHAUST CHECK BALL —
   (Located in Control Valve and Pump Assembly)
2. DIRECT CLUTCH ACCUMULATOR CHECK BALL —
   (Check balls 2-6 located in case cover).
3. LO 1st CHECK BALL.
4. LO AND REVERSE CHECK BALL.
5. DIRECT CLUTCH AND REVERSE CHECK BALL.
6. RNDI AND DETENT CHECK BALL.

Figure 87 - Typical 125 Control Valve Pump Assembly

TYPICAL VALVE BODY SPACER PLATE

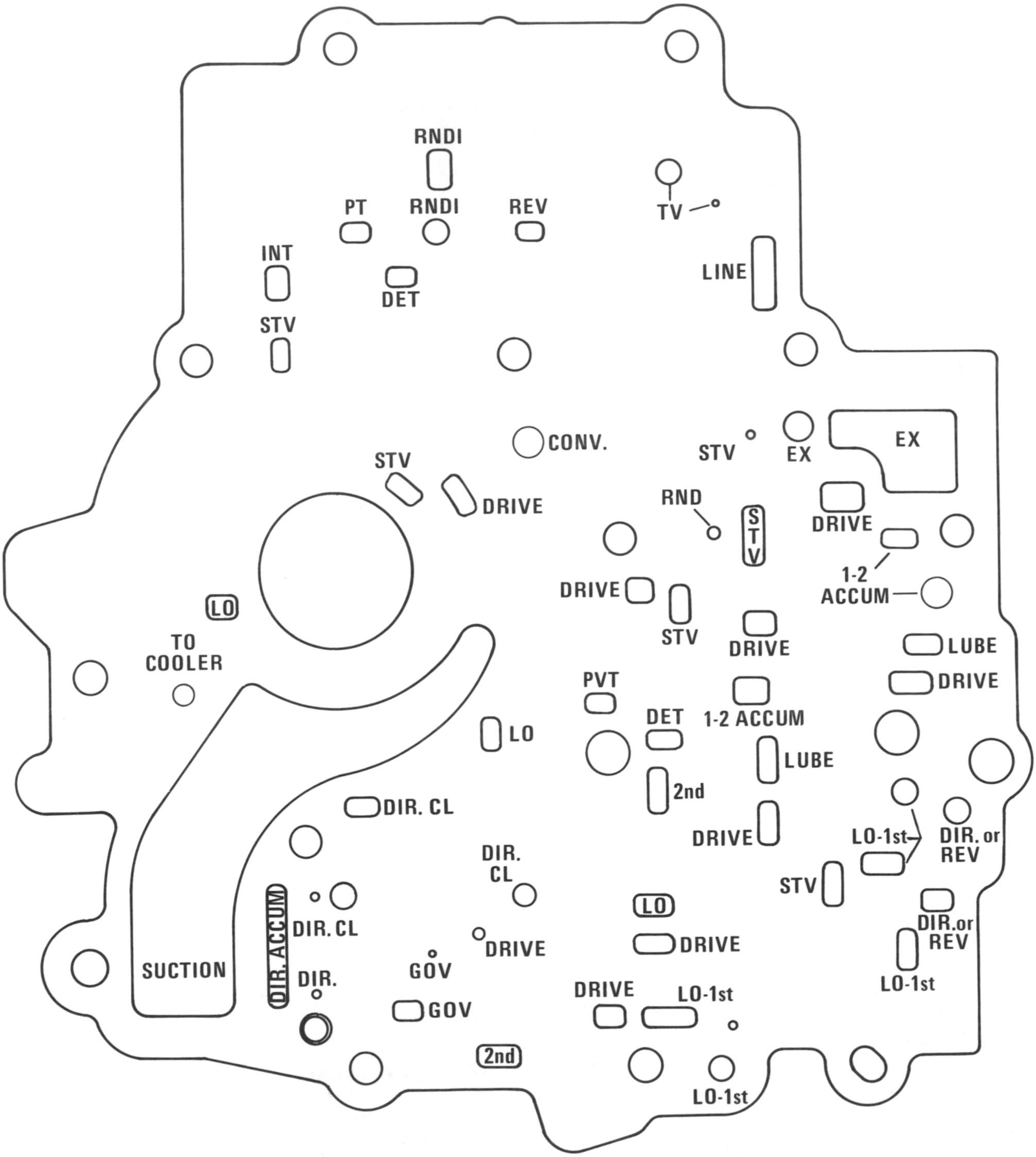

RNDI

PT   RNDI   REV   TV

INT   DET   LINE

STV

CONV.   STV   EX   EX

STV   DRIVE   RND   ⒮ⓉⓋ   DRIVE

LO   DRIVE   1-2 ACCUM

TO COOLER   STV   DRIVE   LUBE

DRIVE

PVT   DET   1-2 ACCUM

LO   LUBE

2nd

DIR. CL   DRIVE   LO-1st   DIR. or REV

DIR. CL   STV

DIR. ACCUM   DIR. CL   LO   DRIVE   DIR. or REV

SUCTION   DIR.   GOV   DRIVE   LO-1st

GOV   DRIVE   LO-1st

2nd   LO-1st

Figure 88 - Valve Body To Case Cover Spacer Plate

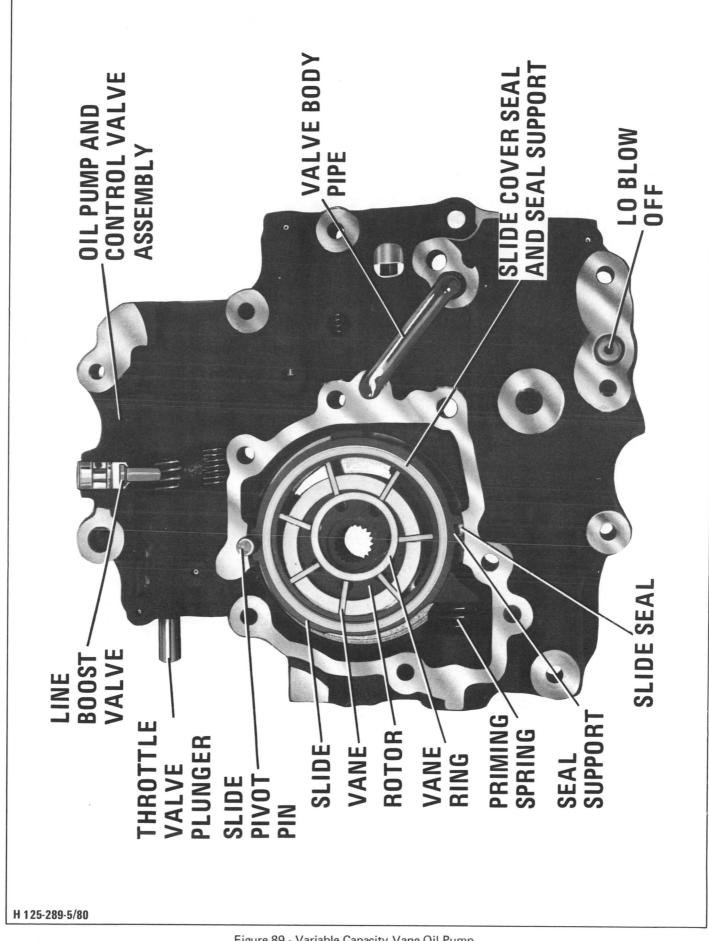

OIL PUMP AND CONTROL VALVE ASSEMBLY

VALVE BODY PIPE

SLIDE COVER SEAL AND SEAL SUPPORT

LO BLOW OFF

LINE BOOST VALVE

THROTTLE VALVE PLUNGER

SLIDE PIVOT PIN

SLIDE

VANE

ROTOR

VANE RING

PRIMING SPRING

SEAL SUPPORT

SLIDE SEAL

H 125-289-5/80

Figure 89 - Variable Capacity Vane Oil Pump

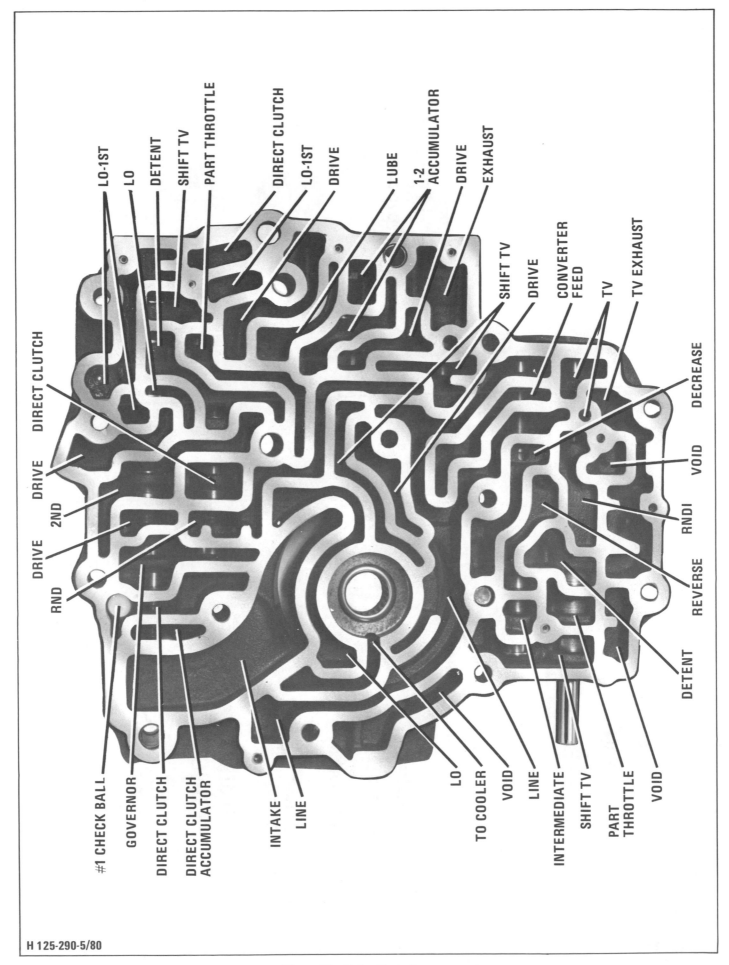

Figure 90 - Valve Body Passages

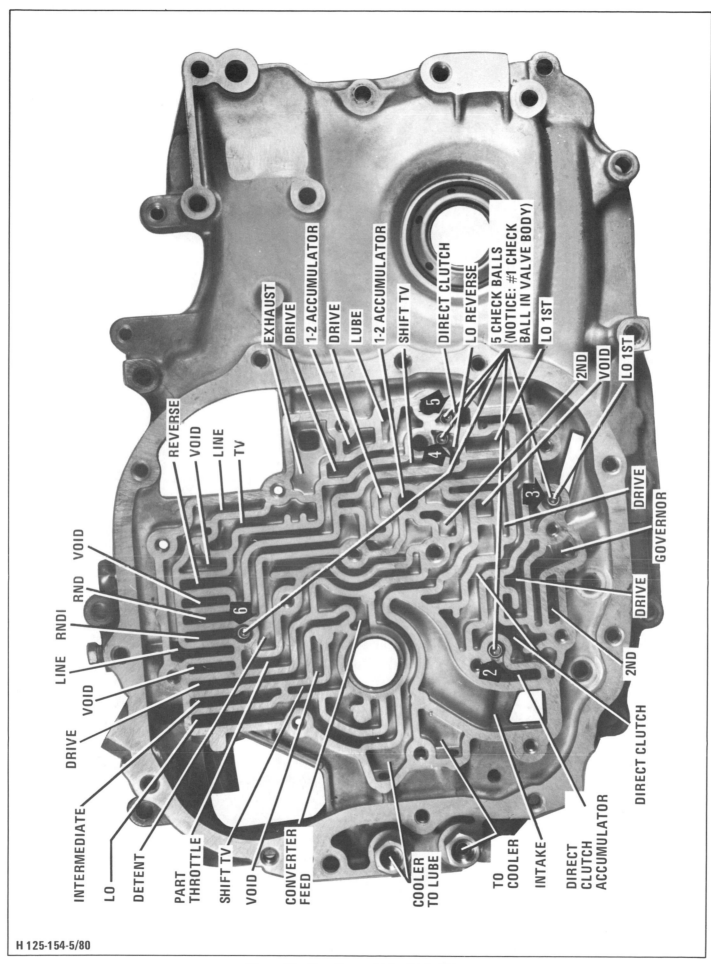

Figure 91 - Case Cover—Valve Body Side

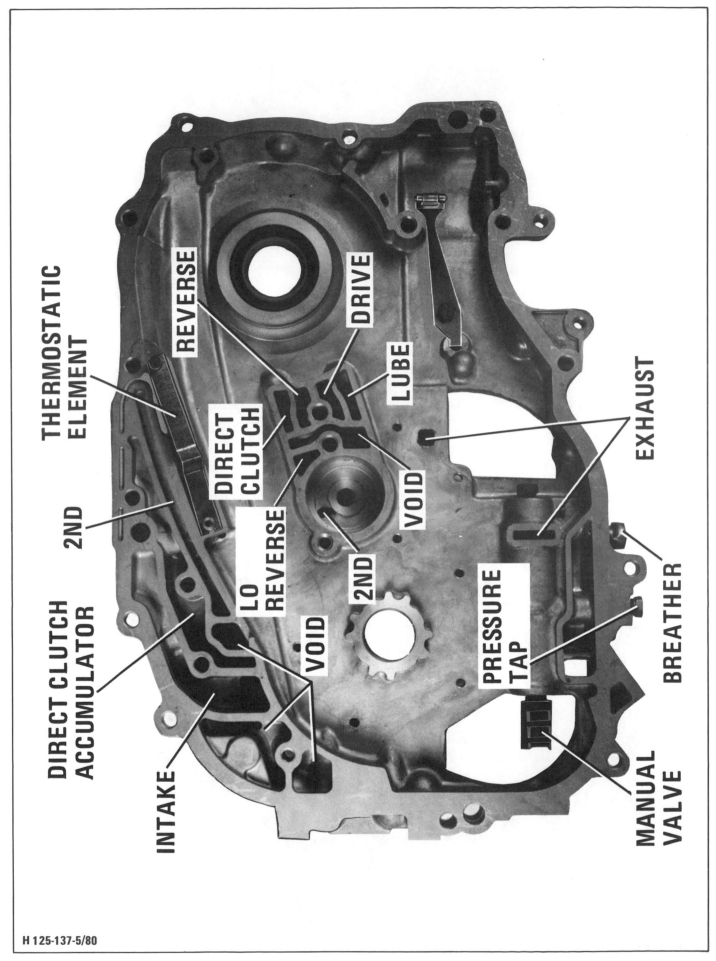

Figure 92 - Case Cover—Case Side

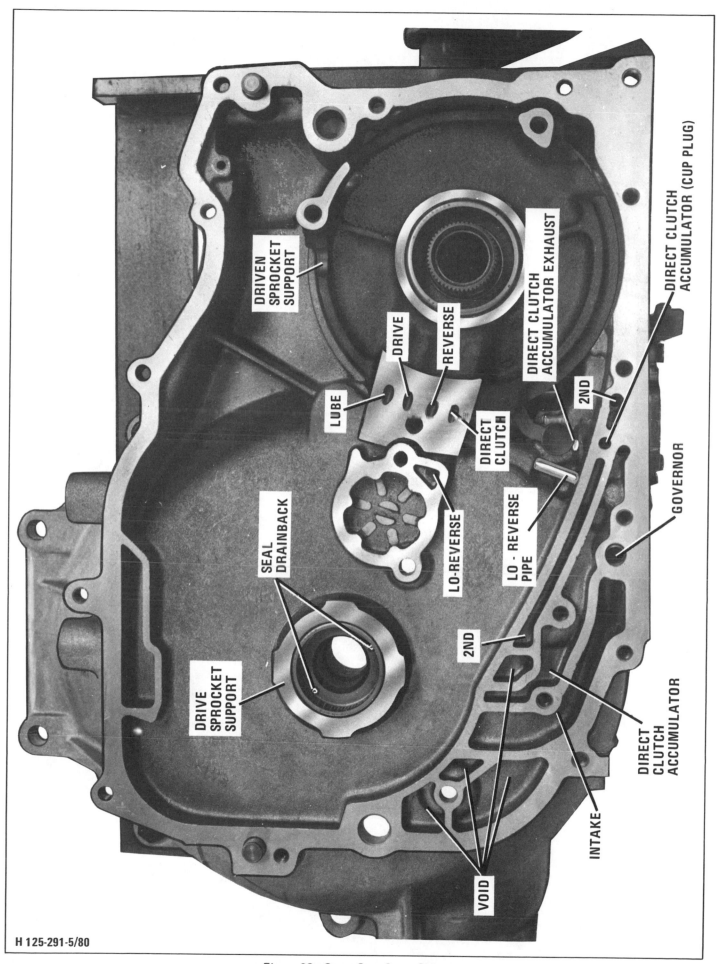

Figure 93 - Case—Case Cover Side

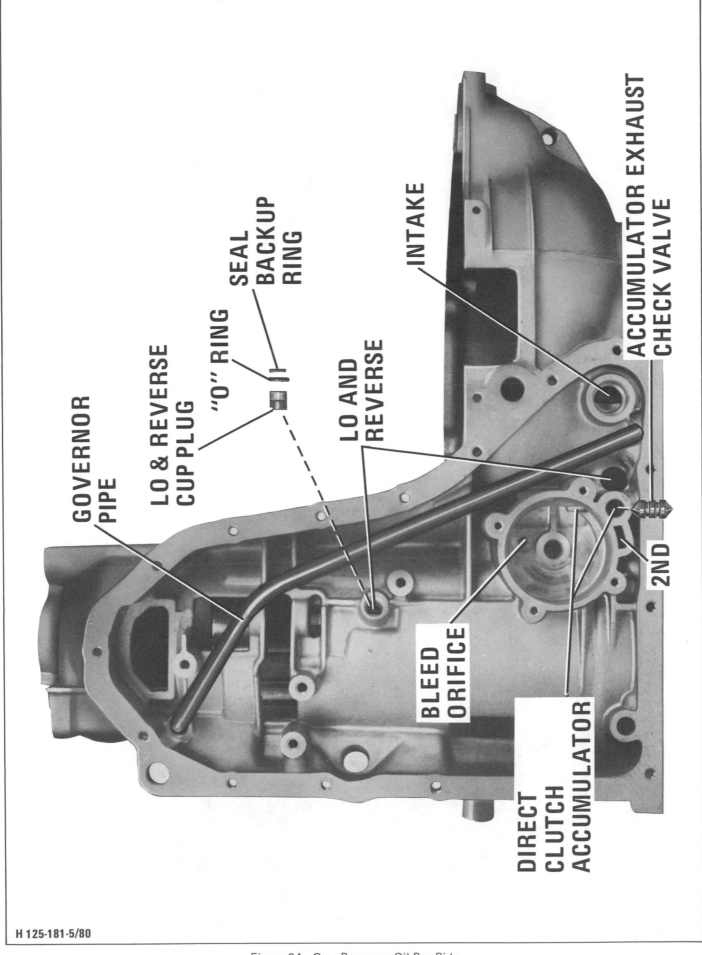

GOVERNOR PIPE

LO & REVERSE CUP PLUG

"O" RING

SEAL BACKUP RING

LO AND REVERSE

INTAKE

ACCUMULATOR EXHAUST CHECK VALVE

2ND

BLEED ORIFICE

DIRECT CLUTCH ACCUMULATOR

Figure 94 - Case Passages—Oil Pan Side

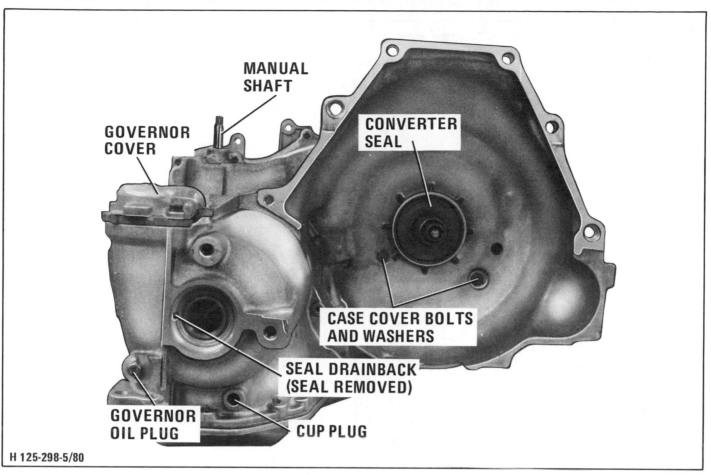

Figure 95 - Case—Right Hand Axle End

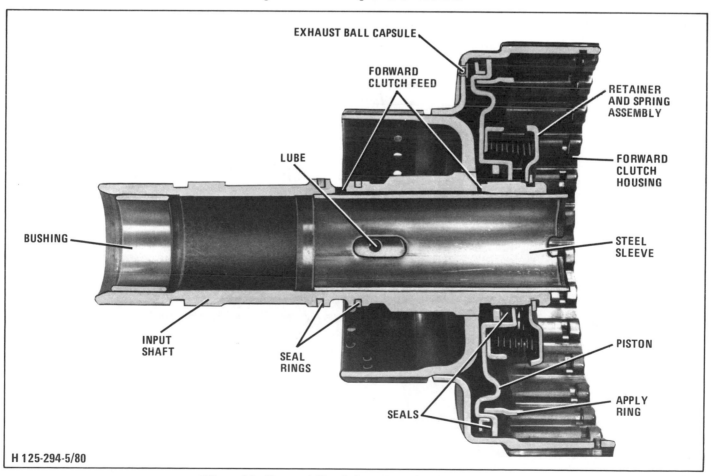

Figure 96 - Forward Clutch Assembly—Cut-Away View

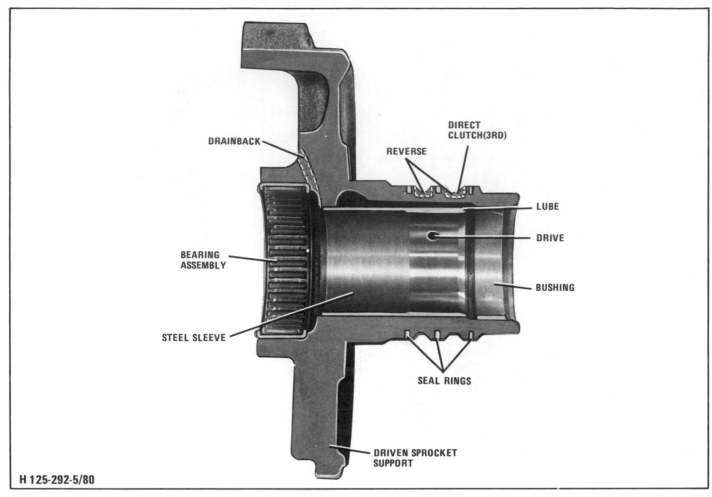

H 125-292-5/80

Figure 97 - Driven Sprocket Support Cut-Away

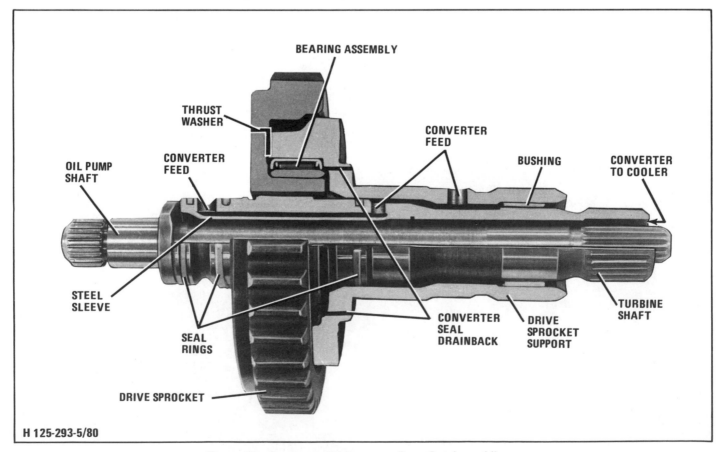

H 125-293-5/80

Figure 98 - Converter Oil Passages—Parts Cut-Away View

114

AXLE JOINT RETAINING RING

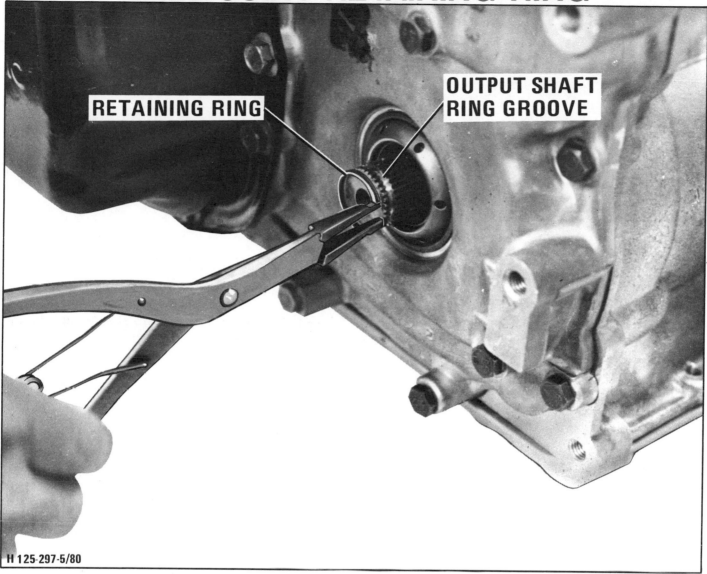

RETAINING RING

OUTPUT SHAFT RING GROOVE

H 125-297-5/80

Figure 99 - Installing Axle Joint Retaining Ring

NOTICE: Expand the axle joint retaining ring only the minimum amount required for proper installation on the output shaft ring groove. Over expanding this ring will make it difficult to install or remove the axle shaft.

ON-CAR WHEEL BALANCING

The suspension should not be allowed to hang free. When the CV joint is run at a very high angle, extra vibrations can occur as well as damage to seals and joints.

The lower control arm should be supported as far outboard as possible.

If the above method is not used, front tires should be balanced on rear positions, or on an off-car balancer.

NOTICE: Front wheels should be spun with the engine. Follow caution (below) 35 m.p.h. (56 km/h) drive wheel speed limit.

CAUTION: On front wheel drive cars drive wheel spin should be limited to 35 m.p.h. (56 km/h) as indicated on the speedometer. This limit is necessary because the speedometer only indicates one-half on the actual wheel speed when one drive wheel is spinning and the other drive wheel is stopped. Unless care is taken in limiting drive wheel spin, the spinning wheel can reach excessive speeds. This may cause excessive differential gear to differential carrier damage which may be diagnosed as a noise in all drive ranges.

DRIVEN SPROCKET SUPPORT SERVICE

A design change was made on the THM 125 Driven Sprocket Support to eliminate a possible bolt torque loss. This change also effected the case to case cover gaskets and driven sprocket to driven sprocket support thrust washer. Improper combinations of those parts will result in erratic shifts due to internal leaks, between mating surfaces.

Refer to the procedure below and the figures on the following page for the proper service information.

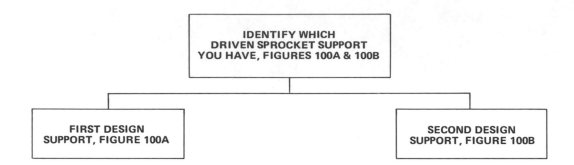

1. Apply Loctite 515 to both sides of the Second Design Case Cover Gasket and install, Figure 101B.

2. Install the Second Design Center Case Gasket, Figure 101B.

3. Install the First Design Service Thrust Washer, Figure 102C.

The First Design Gaskets (Figure 101A) and First Design Thrust Washer (Figure 102A) are no longer serviced and should not be reused. They must be replaced by using the currently released service parts.

NOTICE: Torque all driven sprocket support bolts to 24 n·m (18 ft.-lbs.).

1. Apply Loctite 515 to both sides of the Second Design Case Cover Gasket and install, Figure 101B.

2. Install the Second Design Center Case Gasket, Figure 101B.

3. Install the Second Design Thrust Washer, Figure 102B.

DRIVEN SPROCKET SUPPORT

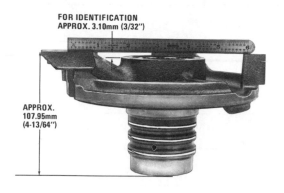

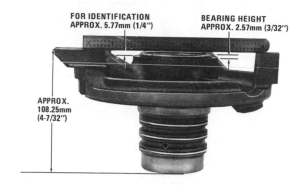

Figure 100A - First Design

Figure 100B - Second Design

CASE TO CASE COVER GASKET
CASE TO CASE COVER CENTER GASKET

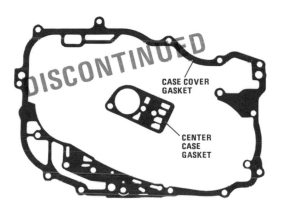

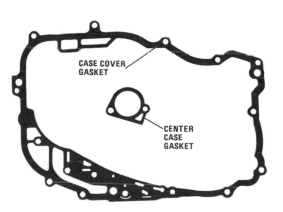

Figure 101A - First Design

Figure 101B - Second Design

DRIVEN SPROCKET TO DRIVEN SPROCKET SUPPORT
THRUST WASHER

Figure 102A - First Design—White

Figure 102C - First Design Service—Red

Figure 102B - Second Design—Black

NOTES

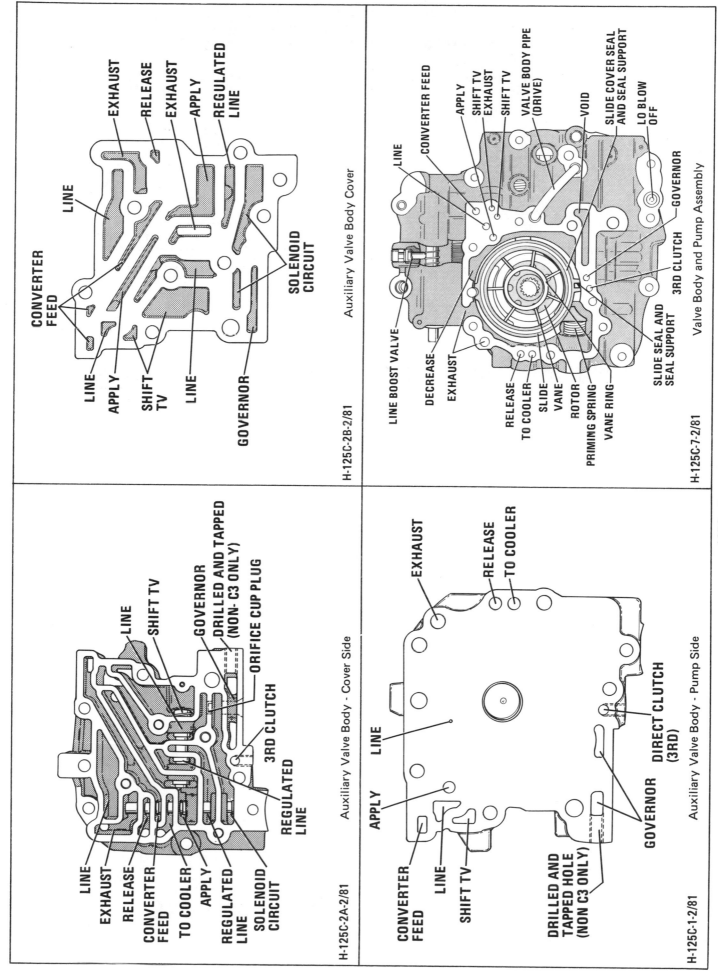

Top-left panel:

EXHAUST
RELEASE
EXHAUST
APPLY
REGULATED LINE

LINE

CONVERTER FEED

SOLENOID CIRCUIT

LINE
APPLY
SHIFT TV
LINE
GOVERNOR

Auxiliary Valve Body Cover

H-125C-2B-2/81

Top-right panel:

LINE
CONVERTER FEED
APPLY
SHIFT TV EXHAUST
SHIFT TV
VALVE BODY PIPE (DRIVE)
VOID
SLIDE COVER SEAL AND SEAL SUPPORT
LO BLOW OFF
GOVERNOR

LINE BOOST VALVE
DECREASE
EXHAUST
RELEASE
TO COOLER
SLIDE
VANE
ROTOR
PRIMING SPRING
VANE RING
SLIDE SEAL AND SEAL SUPPORT
3RD CLUTCH

Valve Body and Pump Assembly

H-125C-7-2/81

Bottom-left panel:

LINE
SHIFT TV
GOVERNOR
DRILLED AND TAPPED (NON- C3 ONLY)
ORIFICE CUP PLUG
3RD CLUTCH
REGULATED LINE

LINE
EXHAUST
RELEASE
CONVERTER FEED
TO COOLER
APPLY
REGULATED LINE
SOLENOID CIRCUIT

Auxiliary Valve Body - Cover Side

H-125C-2A-2/81

Bottom-right panel:

EXHAUST
RELEASE
TO COOLER

APPLY   LINE

CONVERTER FEED
LINE
SHIFT TV
DRILLED AND TAPPED HOLE (NON C3 ONLY)
GOVERNOR
DIRECT CLUTCH (3RD)

Auxiliary Valve Body - Pump Side

H-125C-1-2/81

125C - Components

119

TRANSMISSION CONVERTER CLUTCH (T.C.C.)
ELECTRICAL DIAGNOSIS
CARS EQUIPPED WITH COMPUTER COMMAND CONTROL (C.C.C.)

Mechanical checks such as linkage, oil level, etc., should be performed prior to using this chart. Also, check for a Code 24. If present, see Chart 24 of the Service Manual.

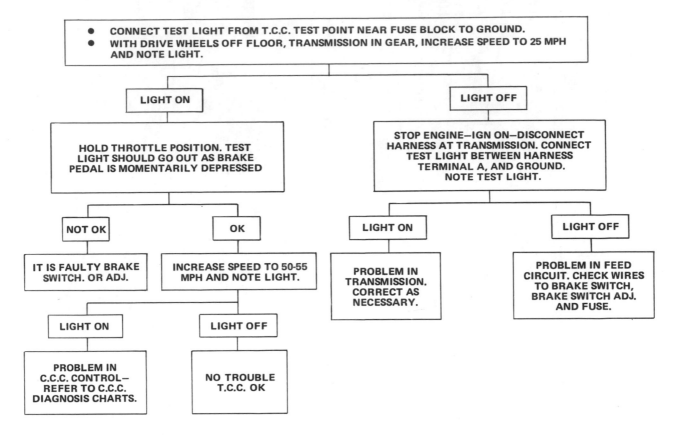

TRANSMISSION CONVERTER CLUTCH (T.C.C.)
ELECTRICAL DIAGNOSIS
CARS NOT EQUIPPED WITH COMPUTER COMMAND CONTROL

Mechanical checks, such as linkage, oil level, etc., should be performed prior to using this chart.

- CONNECT TEST LIGHT FROM T.C.C. TEST POINT NEAR FUSE BLOCK TO GROUND.
- START ENGINE AND RUN AT 1500 RPM IN PARK.
- NOTE LIGHT.

LIGHT ON

HOLD THROTTLE POSITION. TEST LIGHT SHOULD GO OUT AS BRAKE PEDAL IS MOMENTARILY DEPRESSED.

NOT OK

IT IS FAULTY BRAKE SWITCH OR ADJ.

OK

PROBLEM IN TRANSMISSION. REPAIR AS NECESSARY

LIGHT OFF

- CHECK FOR BLOWN FUSE.
- CHECK OPERATION OF BRAKE SWITCH.
- CHECK OPERATION OF VACUUM SWITCH—
  SWITCH OPEN—WITH ENGINE OFF.
  SWITCH CLOSED—AT PART THROTTLE.
  SWITCH OPEN—AT HEAVY FULL THROTTLE.
- CHECK FOR OPENS IN HARNESS.
- CHECK OPERATION OF VRV—
  CLOSED—AT IDLE AND PART THROTTLE.
  OPEN—AT HEAVY FULL THROTTLE.